Bellwork®
Reading/Language Arts

Level 4

Bellwork®
educational solutions

Author
Anne Gall

Contributing Author
Michelle N. Barnett

Editorial Consultants:
Kent A. De Pue
Carrie Hernandez
Erica Kaiser
Margaret Kinney

Illustrator
José L. de la Rosa

The publisher wishes to thank the following educators who read portions of the series prior to publication for their comments and suggestions.

Rebecca Afghani	Ann DePierro	Lauren Rips
Linda Behrens	Victor Dorff	Ona L. Sandi
Pam Bluestein	Don Felton	Mindi Shapiro
Amy Brophy	Kim Fortune	Lynne Shisbey
Sue Buttera	Robin Harbeck	Ruthie Smith
Mary Johnson Cajiao	Sheri Joseph	Kim Marra Stephenson
Mark Cohen	Rebecca Keene	Kathy Terndrup
Marne Colby	Mia Lewis	Alicia Trent
Erika Daniels	Sarah Milam	Jennifer Williams
Carey Davis	Dennis Regus	

Bellwork
921 Mariner Street
Brea, CA 92821-3827

(800) 782-8869
Fax (714) 482-2379
www.bellwork.com

Printed in the U.S.A. (03/11) #33203
ISBN 978-1-932469-24-0

Name _____

For each number below, choose the one that will make a *telling sentence* (statement).

❶ _____ **away on his back.**

   Ⓐ The otter swam
   Ⓑ Swam the otter
   Ⓒ The otter was swim

❸ _____ **a big dinner.**

   Ⓐ The ballplayers
   Ⓑ The ballplayers ate
   Ⓒ Ballplayers ate the

❷ _____ **down the snowbank.**

   Ⓕ Sarah slid
   Ⓖ Did Sarah slide
   Ⓗ Sarah almost

❹ _____ **shining brightly.**

   Ⓕ The sun is
   Ⓖ Is the sun
   Ⓗ The noonday sun

Name _____

Fill in the bubble next to the two words that make up each <u>underlined word</u> (compound word).

❶ <u>afternoon</u>

Ⓐ aft + ernoon

Ⓑ aftern + oon

Ⓒ after + noon

Ⓓ afterno + on

❷ <u>downtown</u>

Ⓕ down + town

Ⓖ do + wntown

Ⓗ downt + own

Ⓚ dow + ntown

❸ <u>bandstand</u>

Ⓐ ban + dstand

Ⓑ band + stand

Ⓒ bandst + and

Ⓓ bands + tand

❹ <u>bedtime</u>

Ⓕ be + dtime

Ⓖ bedt + ime

Ⓗ bedti + me

Ⓚ bed + time

Name _____

Fill in the bubble in front of the verb that goes best with each noun.

❶ The door _____ open.

Ⓐ are
Ⓑ is
Ⓒ were
Ⓓ were not

❷ The gates _____ closed.

Ⓕ are
Ⓖ is
Ⓗ was
Ⓙ was not

❸ My baby sister _____ me every day.

Ⓐ hugs
Ⓑ hug
Ⓒ hugging
Ⓓ has hug

❹ The monkeys _____ around the cage.

Ⓕ climbs
Ⓖ climbing
Ⓗ has climbed
Ⓙ climbed

3

Name _____

For each sentence, fill in the bubble next to the word that is spelled correctly, and fits best in the blank.

1 **He is in the _____ grade.**

Ⓐ first
Ⓑ ferst
Ⓒ forst
Ⓓ furst

2 **She gets _____ grades.**

Ⓕ gowd
Ⓖ goud
Ⓗ good
Ⓙ goid

3 **Which _____ did they go?**

Ⓐ wai
Ⓑ way
Ⓒ wae
Ⓓ waa

4 **He wants to sit _____ the door.**

Ⓕ neer
Ⓖ neyr
Ⓗ neir
Ⓙ near

Name _____

Read each sentence and look at the <u>underlined words</u>. There may be a mistake in them. Select the best answer to correct the mistake. If there is no mistake, select *correct as is*.

---

❶ I like <u>them dogs</u>.

   Ⓐ these here dogs
   Ⓑ these dogs
   Ⓒ this dogs
   Ⓓ correct as is

---

❷ <u>Elizabeth and Emily are</u> learning to sew.

   Ⓕ Elizabeth and Emily is
   Ⓖ Elizabeth and Emily was
   Ⓗ Elizabeth and Emily am
   Ⓙ correct as is

---

❸ <u>The tow of them</u> are having fun.

   Ⓐ The to of them
   Ⓑ The too of them
   Ⓒ The two of them
   Ⓓ correct as is

---

❹ Mother ordered tamales from <u>Mr.s Gonzales</u>.

   Ⓕ Mrs. Gonzales
   Ⓖ Mrs Gonzales
   Ⓗ mrs Gonzales
   Ⓙ correct as is

5

Name _____

Choose the word that comes *first* in alphabetical order.

❶

- Ⓐ boar
- Ⓑ bear
- Ⓒ buffalo
- Ⓓ bird

❸

- Ⓐ snail
- Ⓑ snake
- Ⓒ spider
- Ⓓ seal

❷

- Ⓕ monkey
- Ⓖ mule
- Ⓗ manatee
- Ⓙ mole

❹

- Ⓕ duck
- Ⓖ drake
- Ⓗ deer
- Ⓙ doe

Name _____

For each item below, choose the word that *means the same or almost the same* (synonym) as the <u>underlined word</u>.

❶ to <u>do</u> is to —

Ⓐ act
Ⓑ don't
Ⓒ dog
Ⓓ didn't

❷ <u>double</u> means —

Ⓕ doubt
Ⓖ doable
Ⓗ twice
Ⓙ during

❸ <u>found</u> means —

Ⓐ fought
Ⓑ fair
Ⓒ fine
Ⓓ discovered

❹ <u>fresh</u> means —

Ⓕ new
Ⓖ fried
Ⓗ old
Ⓙ almost

7

Read the passage below. Then answer the questions on the next page. You may look back at this page as you answer the questions.

It's fun to see candy being made in a factory. The ingredients are blended by very large mixers in huge steel vats. The mixture is poured into smaller forms and sent by conveyor belt to be wrapped and packed for shipment. Some people make candy at home too.

I like candy. I like chocolate candy, caramel candy, peppermint candy, and licorice candy. Many years ago you could buy a big candy bar for a nickel and a handful of candy for two cents.

Maybe it's a good thing that candy costs more now. Doctors say it isn't good for us to eat lots of candy. It can cause our teeth to rot, it can make us fat, and it can lead to heart disease. Eating less candy can be better for my body and for my allowance.

Name _____

1 **You can tell from this passage that the author —**

Ⓐ enjoys candy.

Ⓑ hates candy.

Ⓒ makes candy.

Ⓓ will get fat.

2 **Candy used to —**

Ⓕ cost more.

Ⓖ cost less.

Ⓗ cost the same.

Ⓙ cost a dime.

3 **You can tell that doctors think —**

Ⓐ chocolate candy tastes best.

Ⓑ candy is cheap.

Ⓒ eating too much candy is bad for you.

Ⓓ candy is good for you.

4 **Many years ago, a handful of candy cost —**

Ⓕ a nickel.

Ⓖ three cents.

Ⓗ more than a big candy bar.

Ⓙ less than a big candy bar.

9

Name _____

Fill in the bubble next to the words that are capitalized correctly.

❶ My cousin lives in —

- Ⓐ north carolina.
- Ⓑ North carolina.
- Ⓒ North Carolina.
- Ⓓ north Carolina.

❷ Winter vacation comes during —

- Ⓕ December and January.
- Ⓖ December and january.
- Ⓗ december and January.
- Ⓙ december and january.

❸ Lindbergh was first to fly across the _____ alone.

- Ⓐ atlantic ocean
- Ⓑ Atlantic ocean
- Ⓒ atlantic Ocean
- Ⓓ Atlantic Ocean

❹ _____ always comes on February 14.

- Ⓕ valentine's day
- Ⓖ Valentine's day
- Ⓗ valentine's Day
- Ⓙ Valentine's Day

Name _____

Fill in the bubble next to the words needed to make a complete sentence.

❶ The elephant _____.

Ⓐ ate the peanuts
Ⓑ we threw
Ⓒ in the zoo
Ⓓ hungry

❷ At six o'clock, we will _____.

Ⓕ ate supper
Ⓖ eat supper
Ⓗ went to the show
Ⓙ had supper

❸ _____ slowly.

Ⓐ Snails move
Ⓑ Snails will
Ⓒ Snails moves
Ⓓ Snails was

❹ Yesterday, _____ a good time.

Ⓕ I am having
Ⓖ I have
Ⓗ I had
Ⓙ I having

11

Name _____

1 **Mark the word that has the same sound as the <u>u</u> in <u>u</u>sed.**

Ⓐ us

Ⓑ you

Ⓒ burst

Ⓓ fun

2 **Mark the word that has the same sound as the <u>ow</u> in bel<u>ow</u>.**

Ⓕ coat

Ⓖ boy

Ⓗ join

Ⓙ won

3 **Mark the word that has the same sound as the <u>e</u> in k<u>e</u>pt.**

Ⓐ here

Ⓑ met

Ⓒ feet

Ⓓ great

4 **Mark the word that has the same sound as the <u>ea</u> in str<u>ea</u>m.**

Ⓕ still

Ⓖ line

Ⓗ while

Ⓙ field

Name _____

Read each sentence. Fill in the bubble next to the meaning of the <u>underlined contraction</u>.

❶ I <u>couldn't</u> get home on time.

   Ⓐ cold not

   Ⓑ could know

   Ⓒ could not

   Ⓓ could now

❷ <u>We'll</u> go on a field trip Tuesday morning.

   Ⓕ We ill

   Ⓖ We all

   Ⓗ Will we

   Ⓙ We will

❸ Fernando <u>didn't</u> catch the bus.

   Ⓐ dint

   Ⓑ did not

   Ⓒ did out

   Ⓓ do not

❹ My sister <u>shouldn't</u> stay out so late at night.

   Ⓕ should

   Ⓖ shoulder not

   Ⓗ should not

   Ⓙ could not

13

Name _____

Read each sentence and look at the underlined words. There may be a mistake in them. Select the best answer to correct the mistake. If there is no mistake, select *correct as is*.

❶ Phillip walker his dog after school.

 Ⓐ Phillip walk
 Ⓑ Phillip walking
 Ⓒ Phillip walked
 Ⓓ correct as is

❷ He is a very hard works.

 Ⓕ a very hard worker
 Ⓖ a very hard worked
 Ⓗ a very hard working
 Ⓙ correct as is

❸ José played catcher on him team.

 Ⓐ there team
 Ⓑ he team
 Ⓒ his team
 Ⓓ correct as is

❹ Amber and Anna is eating lunch together.

 Ⓕ Amber and Anna where
 Ⓖ Amber and Anna was
 Ⓗ Amber and Anna were
 Ⓙ correct as is

14

Name _____

Read each paragraph. Then fill in the bubble next to the sentence that goes *best* in the paragraph.

❶   **Nghia is in a troop. He attends every meeting, has gone to camp, and has earned many badges.**

_____

Ⓐ Nghia is a good boy.

Ⓑ Nghia likes being in the troop.

Ⓒ Nghia wants to be a policeman.

Ⓓ The troop meets at school.

❷   **Karen likes to write stories. _____ _____ She writes about rabbits, squirrels, beavers, and otters.**

Ⓕ She likes animal stories.

Ⓖ She reads a lot.

Ⓗ She has many pets.

Ⓙ She plays outdoors.

15

Name _____

Fill in the bubble next to the word that correctly completes each sentence.

1 There are four _____ on the shelf.

Ⓐ bookes
Ⓑ books
Ⓒ bookys
Ⓓ bookies

2 Those _____ have sharp claws.

Ⓕ cates
Ⓖ caties
Ⓗ cats
Ⓙ catts

3 The red _____ are blooming now.

Ⓐ roses
Ⓑ rosies
Ⓒ ross
Ⓓ rosys

4 These _____ must be signed.

Ⓕ paperys
Ⓖ paperes
Ⓗ paperies
Ⓙ papers

16

Name _____

Fill in the bubble next to the answer with the correct punctuation mark.

❶ I _____ want to go to school.

Ⓐ do'nt

Ⓑ don't

Ⓒ donot

Ⓓ dont'

❷ Her birthday is —

Ⓕ October 14 1996.

Ⓖ October. 14 1996.

Ⓗ October 14, 1996.

Ⓙ October 14. 1996.

❸ _____ Nguyen is a nice lady.

Ⓐ Mrs

Ⓑ Mrs.

Ⓒ Mrs,

Ⓓ Mr's

❹ We had fun at the —

Ⓕ party.

Ⓖ party?

Ⓗ par'ty

Ⓙ party"

17

Read the passage below. Then answer the questions on the next page. You may look back at this page as you answer the questions.

How often do you eat bread? How many kinds have you eaten? Do you like to try new <u>varieties</u> of bread products?

Before there were so many supermarkets in this country, many families ate only homemade bread. Since "store bought" bread has been so easy to buy and is so convenient to use, many people have never tasted bread baked at home.

Cakes, cookies, doughnuts, rolls, pancakes, and buns for hamburgers and hot dogs are all made with flour. Therefore, they are all bread products.

The next time you're in the grocery store or bakery, see how many kinds of bread products you can find.

Name _____

① **Most bread products are —**

Ⓐ boiled.

Ⓑ fried.

Ⓒ made with flour.

Ⓓ cookies.

② **Which came first?**

Ⓕ store bought bread

Ⓖ pizza

Ⓗ hot dog buns

Ⓙ homemade bread

③ **This passage mainly tells —**

Ⓐ that there are many kinds of bread products.

Ⓑ that "store bought" means made at the store.

Ⓒ how to make bread at home.

Ⓓ which breads are good for you.

④ **In this passage varieties means —**

Ⓕ tries.

Ⓖ very.

Ⓗ kinds.

Ⓙ varies.

19

Name _____

Fill in the bubble next to the word (antonym) that correctly completes each sentence.

❶ The *opposite* of <u>pull</u> is —

Ⓐ tug.
Ⓑ push.
Ⓒ haul.
Ⓓ lug.

❸ The *opposite* of <u>much</u> is —

Ⓐ bunch.
Ⓑ many.
Ⓒ lot.
Ⓓ little.

❷ The *opposite* of <u>love</u> is —

Ⓕ hate.
Ⓖ adore.
Ⓗ admire.
Ⓙ live.

❹ The *opposite* of <u>most</u> is —

Ⓕ much.
Ⓖ many.
Ⓗ less.
Ⓙ least.

Name _____

Fill in the bubble next to the answer that correctly completes each sentence.

❶ _____ a mountain yesterday.

Ⓐ He up
Ⓑ He climbed
Ⓒ He will
Ⓓ He down

❷ _____ South for the winter.

Ⓕ The birds
Ⓖ Flying birds
Ⓗ The birds have
Ⓙ The birds flew

❸ _____ visit Grandmother.

Ⓐ I can
Ⓑ Can
Ⓒ I am
Ⓓ On Tuesday

❹ The doctor _____.

Ⓕ in his office
Ⓖ is in his office
Ⓗ his office
Ⓙ has office

22

Name _____

Fill in the bubble next to the word that rhymes with each <u>underlined word</u>.

❶ <u>go</u>

- Ⓐ know
- Ⓑ now
- Ⓒ not
- Ⓓ cow

❷ <u>song</u>

- Ⓕ son
- Ⓖ long
- Ⓗ sound
- Ⓙ soon

❸ <u>there</u>

- Ⓐ then
- Ⓑ hair
- Ⓒ here
- Ⓓ they

❹ <u>never</u>

- Ⓕ ever
- Ⓖ lover
- Ⓗ even
- Ⓙ beaver

21

Name _____

Fill in the bubble next to the prefix that correctly completes each sentence.

1 Papa was ____pleased with my bad grades.

Ⓐ un-
Ⓑ mis-
Ⓒ dis-
Ⓓ re-

2 That answer is wrong; you need to ____think the problem.

Ⓕ un-
Ⓖ re-
Ⓗ im-
Ⓙ ex-

3 A ___angle has three sides.

Ⓐ bi-
Ⓑ tri-
Ⓒ uni-
Ⓓ pre-

4 Please ___lock the door.

Ⓕ un-
Ⓖ mis-
Ⓗ dis-
Ⓙ ex-

Read the passage below. Then answer the questions on the next page. You may look back at this page as you answer the questions.

Bees live in many parts of the world. There are thousands of kinds of bees, but only honeybees make honey. Bees help flowers, vegetables, and humans by carrying pollen from blossom to blossom. Many plants would die if they were not visited by bees. <u>Bumblebees</u> are bigger than honeybees.

Many people are afraid of bees because their sting can be very painful. A bee sting can even be <u>fatal</u>, causing death to a person who is allergic to bees or who receives several hundred stings. For most people, however, the pain and itching stops after a day or two.

Don't scream or move suddenly if bees come around. Just walk away quietly and slowly.

Name _____

1 **The two words in <u>bumblebee</u> are —**

Ⓐ bum + blebee.
Ⓑ bumble + bee.
Ⓒ bumble + be.

3 **Honeybees are _____ bumblebees.**

Ⓐ larger than
Ⓑ smaller than
Ⓒ the same size as

2 **The word <u>fatal</u> means —**

Ⓕ causing pain.
Ⓖ causing death.
Ⓗ making honey.

4 **Around bees you should —**

Ⓕ run away fast.
Ⓖ scream for help.
Ⓗ be careful.

29

Name _____

Fill in the bubble next to the word that correctly completes each sentence.

❶ She said her cat has nine _____.

Ⓐ lives
Ⓑ lifes
Ⓒ live's
Ⓓ lives'

❷ My grandmother traveled to many _____.

Ⓕ places
Ⓖ placs
Ⓗ plases
Ⓙ playses

❸ Nine _____ are on the baseball team.

Ⓐ mans
Ⓑ men
Ⓒ man
Ⓓ mens

❹ We saw many _____ in the forest.

Ⓕ deer
Ⓖ deeres
Ⓗ deers
Ⓙ deeries

Name _____

Fill in the bubble next to the sentence that is correctly capitalized.

1
- Ⓐ Our class took a Field Trip to the Museum of Natural Artifacts.
- Ⓑ Our class took a field trip to the Museum of Natural Artifacts.
- Ⓒ Our class took a field trip to the museum of natural artifacts.

2
- Ⓕ My mom is a member of the Parent Volunteer Association.
- Ⓖ My mom is a Member of the parent volunteer Association.
- Ⓗ My mom is a Member of the Parent Volunteer association.

3
- Ⓐ Every month my dad gets his subscription to *Healthy ways* magazine.
- Ⓑ Every month my dad gets his subscription to *healthy ways* Magazine.
- Ⓒ Every month my dad gets his subscription to *Healthy Ways* magazine.

4
- Ⓕ Vincent van Gogh is famous for his painting, *Sunflowers*.
- Ⓖ Vincent van Gogh is famous for his Painting, *Sunflowers*.
- Ⓗ Vincent van Gogh is famous for his painting, *sunflowers*.

31

Name _____

Fill in the bubble next to the word (homophone) that correctly completes each sentence.

1 I _____ the school is getting a new flag.

Ⓐ here
Ⓑ hear

2 Close one _____ when you wink.

Ⓕ eye
Ⓖ I

3 How _____ is the sky?

Ⓐ hi
Ⓑ high

4 Throw the ball over _____.

Ⓕ their
Ⓖ there

5 The teacher said to _____ about our vacation.

Ⓐ write
Ⓑ right

6 How much does that horse _____?

Ⓕ weigh
Ⓖ way

Name _____

Mark the bubble next to the sentence that goes *best* on the blank line in each paragraph.

❶   **The firemen slid down the pole at the firehouse. They put on their boots and coats and climbed in the truck.** _____

   Ⓐ Sirens blew as they headed for the fire.

   Ⓑ The dog ran around the firehouse.

   Ⓒ A fireman answered the telephone.

---

❷   _____ **It came to the side of the tank when the trainer whistled. The trainer rode on his back.**

   Ⓕ The trainer gave him a fish.

   Ⓖ The whale swam back and forth.

   Ⓗ The goldfish swam around and around.

33

Name _____

Read each sentence. Fill in the bubble in front of the word that correctly completes each sentence.

---

1 We need two more _____ in here.

Ⓐ table's
Ⓑ tables
Ⓒ table
Ⓓ tabless

2 The clown will be painting _____ today.

Ⓕ faces
Ⓖ face's
Ⓗ face
Ⓙ faceses

3 Blanca's drawings won two _____.

Ⓐ ribbones
Ⓑ ribbons
Ⓒ ribbon
Ⓓ ribbon's

4 You have two eyes and two _____.

Ⓕ earies
Ⓖ eares
Ⓗ ear
Ⓙ ears

Name _____

For each numbered sentence, choose the words that make it a *question*.

① _____ that movie?

   Ⓐ Have you seen
   Ⓑ Seen have you
   Ⓒ You have seen

③ _____ that game?

   Ⓐ Like did you
   Ⓑ You did like
   Ⓒ Did you like

② _____ to my party?

   Ⓕ You will come
   Ⓖ Will you come
   Ⓗ Come will you

④ _____ to camp?

   Ⓕ Are you going
   Ⓖ Going are you
   Ⓗ You are going

35

Name _____

Read each sentence and look at the <u>underlined words</u>. There may be a mistake in them.
Select the best answer to correct the mistake. If there is no mistake, select *correct as is*.

❶ <u>These books was</u> boring.

    Ⓐ These books is
    Ⓑ These books are
    Ⓒ These books am
    Ⓓ correct as is

❷ I like <u>this science books</u>.

    Ⓕ them science books
    Ⓖ these science books
    Ⓗ that science books
    Ⓙ correct as is

❸ <u>He will going</u> home.

    Ⓐ He was going
    Ⓑ He were going
    Ⓒ He would going
    Ⓓ correct as is

❹ She <u>had and apple</u> in her lunchbox.

    Ⓕ had an apple
    Ⓖ had a apple
    Ⓗ had any apple
    Ⓙ correct as is

36

Name _____

1 **Mark the word that has the same sound as the <u>ou</u> in p<u>ou</u>nd.**

Ⓐ below
Ⓑ would
Ⓒ outside
Ⓓ pool

2 **Mark the word that has the same sound as the <u>ee</u> in f<u>ee</u>t.**

Ⓕ these
Ⓖ left
Ⓗ few
Ⓙ never

3 **Mark the word that has the same sound as the <u>oa</u> in c<u>oa</u>t.**

Ⓐ good
Ⓑ so
Ⓒ one
Ⓓ do

4 **Mark the word that has the same sound as the <u>ow</u> in n<u>ow</u>.**

Ⓕ house
Ⓖ rose
Ⓗ known
Ⓙ show

37

Name _____

Fill in the bubble next to the word with the correct punctuation.

1 Josh carried his _____ pencil, notebook, and books in his backpack.

 Ⓐ pen,
 Ⓑ pen?
 Ⓒ pen'
 Ⓓ pen.

2 The substitute teacher was _____ Wallace.

 Ⓕ Mrs
 Ⓖ Mrs,
 Ⓗ Mrs.
 Ⓙ Mr's

3 Why don't you like _____

 Ⓐ me
 Ⓑ me,
 Ⓒ me.
 Ⓓ me?

4 My father _____ let me go.

 Ⓕ would'nt
 Ⓖ wouldnt'
 Ⓗ wouldnt
 Ⓙ wouldn't

38

Name _____

Fill in the bubble next to the one that is capitalized correctly.

1 **Robert lives on _____.**

Ⓐ Columbia street
Ⓑ Columbia Street
Ⓒ columbia Street
Ⓓ columbia street

2 **_____ are vacation days.**

Ⓕ Friday and Monday
Ⓖ friday and monday
Ⓗ Friday and monday
Ⓙ friday and Monday

3 **There will be no mail on _____.**

Ⓐ labor day
Ⓑ Labor day
Ⓒ labor Day
Ⓓ Labor Day

4 **Water in the _____ is very cold.**

Ⓕ arctic ocean
Ⓖ Arctic ocean
Ⓗ arctic Ocean
Ⓙ Arctic Ocean

39

Read the passage below. Then answer the questions on the next page. You may look back at this page as you answer the questions.

When it rains a little bit, puddles appear on the sidewalk between our classrooms. The girls step around or over them, but some boys like to stomp a foot right in the middle of a puddle and get the girls wet. On weekends when it rains too hard to go outside, we read, play games, or watch TV.

Once we had a flood. Rainwater covered the street and our yard. Water came clear up to our porch. We had to bring the dog inside so he wouldn't drown. The power went off so we had no lights and couldn't cook on our electric stove. But we were lucky; the rain stopped before the water came into our house.

A little rain can be fun, but "too much is too much."

Name _____

1 In this passage some of the boys thought —

Ⓐ a little rain was fun.

Ⓑ a little rain was dangerous.

Ⓒ they'd stay home from school.

2 There was a flood because —

Ⓕ there was not enough rain.

Ⓖ there was no rain.

Ⓗ there was too much rain.

3 They couldn't use their electric stove because —

Ⓐ water came into the house.

Ⓑ the power was off.

Ⓒ they didn't have a microwave oven.

4 "Too much is too much" means that —

Ⓕ it rains a lot on weekends.

Ⓖ a lot of rain can be fun.

Ⓗ a lot of rain can cause trouble.

BELLWORK Reading/Language Arts • Level 4

Name _____

Fill in the bubble next to the root (base) word for each <u>underlined word</u>.

1 The root (base) of the word <u>coming</u> is —

Ⓐ comin.
Ⓑ ing.
Ⓒ come.
Ⓓ co.

2 The root (base) of the word <u>spelled</u> is —

Ⓕ spel.
Ⓖ spell.
Ⓗ ed.
Ⓙ spelle.

3 The root (base) of the word <u>cutting</u> is —

Ⓐ cute.
Ⓑ cutt.
Ⓒ cut.
Ⓓ cuttin.

4 The root (base) of the word <u>seas</u> is —

Ⓕ sea.
Ⓖ see.
Ⓗ as.
Ⓙ ease.

Name _____

For each item below, choose the word that *means the same or almost the same* (synonym) as the <u>underlined word</u>.

❶ <u>folks</u> means —

Ⓐ famous
Ⓑ full
Ⓒ fall
Ⓓ people

❷ a <u>wild</u> horse means —

Ⓕ animal
Ⓖ tame
Ⓗ untamed
Ⓙ will

❸ <u>labor</u> means —

Ⓐ while
Ⓑ work
Ⓒ weary
Ⓓ idle

❹ <u>absent</u> means —

Ⓕ present
Ⓖ advise
Ⓗ away
Ⓙ remainder

43

Name _____

Fill in the bubble next to the word that correctly completes each sentence.

1 The acrobat has _____ down.

    Ⓐ falled
    Ⓑ falling
    Ⓒ fallen
    Ⓓ fell

2 The sign says, "Don't _____ the animals."

    Ⓕ fed
    Ⓖ feed
    Ⓗ feeding
    Ⓙ food

3 The principal _____ to me yesterday.

    Ⓐ speaked
    Ⓑ speaker
    Ⓒ spoken
    Ⓓ spoke

4 That old cat must _____ nine lives.

    Ⓕ having
    Ⓖ has
    Ⓗ had
    Ⓙ have

44

Name _____

Read each sentence and look at the underlined words. There may be a mistake in them.
Select the best answer to correct the mistake. If there is no mistake, select *correct as is*.

---

1 **They has going** to the park.

   Ⓐ They were going
   Ⓑ They was going
   Ⓒ They here going
   Ⓓ correct as is

---

2 Robyn ate lunch with **Amy and she**.

   Ⓕ Amy and I
   Ⓖ Amy and he
   Ⓗ Amy and me
   Ⓙ correct as is

---

3 The **james River** is in Virginia.

   Ⓐ james river
   Ⓑ James river
   Ⓒ James River
   Ⓓ correct as is

---

4 **He has went** home.

   Ⓕ He has going
   Ⓖ He has gone
   Ⓗ He have gone
   Ⓙ correct as is

45

Name _____

For each numbered sentence, choose the words that make it a *question*.

❶ _____ **out to play?**

- Ⓐ Omar can home
- Ⓑ Can Omar come
- Ⓒ Come, Omar
- Ⓓ You come Omar

❸ _____ **the ending of that story?**

- Ⓐ Like you
- Ⓑ Did you like
- Ⓒ Like you did
- Ⓓ You did like

❷ _____ ***The Briar Patch?***

- Ⓕ You read have
- Ⓖ Have read
- Ⓗ Have you read
- Ⓙ Read me about

❹ _____ **gymnast?**

- Ⓕ Is Leah the best
- Ⓖ The best is Leah
- Ⓗ Leah is the best
- Ⓙ Is the best Leah

Name _____

1 **Mark the word that rhymes with grew.**

(A) igloo

(B) howl

(C) greet

(D) grow

2 **Mark the word that rhymes with eight.**

(F) night

(G) bait

(H) beet

(J) cart

3 **Mark the word that rhymes with good.**

(A) boot

(B) would

(C) road

(D) crowd

4 **Mark the word that rhymes with cut.**

(F) cute

(G) out

(H) mutt

(J) skirt

47

Name _____

Fill in the bubble under the *complete subject* of each sentence.

1 <u>Chile and Peru</u>   <u>are in South America</u>.
    Ⓐ   Ⓑ

2 <u>Canaries and parakeets</u> <u>make good pets</u>.
    Ⓕ   Ⓖ

3 <u>All penguins</u>   <u>have short legs</u>.
    Ⓐ   Ⓑ

4 <u>The United States</u> <u>includes fifty states</u>.
    Ⓕ   Ⓖ

Fill in the bubble under the *complete predicate* of each sentence.

5 <u>Chile and Peru</u>   <u>are in South America</u>.
    Ⓐ   Ⓑ

6 <u>Canaries and parakeets</u> <u>make good pets</u>.
    Ⓕ   Ⓖ

7 <u>All penguins</u>   <u>have short legs</u>.
    Ⓐ   Ⓑ

8 <u>The United States</u> <u>includes fifty states</u>.
    Ⓕ   Ⓖ

Name _____

Read each set of sentences and decide if one of the underlined words is spelled incorrectly, or if there is *no mistake*. Choose your answer and fill in the bubble.

1
- Ⓐ Let's go to the <u>movies</u> on Saturday.
- Ⓑ Sarah was <u>cent</u> to a new classroom.
- Ⓒ I am tired of <u>waiting</u> for them.
- Ⓓ no mistake

2
- Ⓕ The fossils that we saw were very well <u>preserved</u>.
- Ⓖ In the <u>storm</u>, a fierce wind blew.
- Ⓗ I'd like to be your <u>friend</u>.
- Ⓙ no mistake

3
- Ⓐ How can we <u>train</u> our bird to talk?
- Ⓑ One good <u>deed</u> deserves another.
- Ⓒ March is a good month to fly <u>kits</u>.
- Ⓓ no mistake

4
- Ⓕ The pine trees are <u>straeght</u> and tall.
- Ⓖ The <u>traffic</u> was terrible today.
- Ⓗ Which colored balloon would you <u>pick</u>?
- Ⓙ no mistake

49

Name _____

Read each paragraph. Then fill in the bubble next to the sentence that goes *best* in the paragraph.

 They went to Texas to look for oil.

_____

They jumped for joy when oil shot out of the second well.

Ⓐ The capital of Texas is Austin.

Ⓑ They drilled a well but found no oil.

Ⓒ Texas is famous for its ranches.

 _____

He rode his bike to school every day, even in the rain.   He rode his bike to the park to do tricks with his friends.

Ⓕ Brian had many friends.

Ⓖ Brian loved to ride his bike.

Ⓗ Brian went to school every day.

Name _____

Fill in the bubble next to the word (antonym) that correctly completes each sentence.

1 The *opposite* of <u>young</u> is —

Ⓐ new.
Ⓑ old.
Ⓒ baby.
Ⓓ middle-aged.

3 The *opposite* of <u>begin</u> is —

Ⓐ start.
Ⓑ end.
Ⓒ arise.
Ⓓ open.

2 The *opposite* of <u>night</u> is —

Ⓕ evening.
Ⓖ midnight.
Ⓗ day.
Ⓙ dark.

4 The *opposite* of <u>light</u> is —

Ⓕ heavy.
Ⓖ near.
Ⓗ hungry.
Ⓙ little.

51

Read the passage below. Then answer the questions on the next page. You may look back at this page as you answer the questions.

The salt you shake onto your food may have come from seawater, from a mine, or from a <u>well</u>. Besides the ocean, the Mediterranean and Caribbean Seas, and some lakes also contain a lot of salt.

Some salt is found on top of the ground and some far underground. In some places it is mined much like coal is mined. In other places, wells are drilled into the ground and water is forced down under the salt. The salt and water then come to the top of the well as <u>brine</u>.

The next time you eat salty potato chips or put salt on your food, you might stop and think about where it came from.

Name _____

❶ This passage *mainly* tells —

Ⓐ where salt comes from.

Ⓑ what salt is used for.

Ⓒ about the Mediterranean Sea.

❷ In this passage the word <u>well</u> means —

Ⓕ not sick.

Ⓖ a place to find salt.

Ⓗ we will.

❸ <u>Brine</u> is —

Ⓐ salt.

Ⓑ water.

Ⓒ salty water.

❹ Salt can be found in —

Ⓕ coal mines.

Ⓖ oil wells.

Ⓗ the ocean.

53

Name _____

Read each set of sentences and decide if one of the <u>underlined words</u> is spelled incorrectly, or if there is *no mistake*. Choose your answer and fill in the bubble.

 1

Ⓐ She said, "Turn off the <u>lihgt</u> and go to sleep."

Ⓑ That is a good <u>reason</u>.

Ⓒ Mom <u>tripped</u> over the toys.

Ⓓ no mistake

 2

Ⓕ The <u>peaches</u> are ripe.

Ⓖ Tim <u>brushs</u> the mare's coat every day.

Ⓗ A <u>customer</u> left the store.

Ⓙ no mistake

 3

Ⓐ When the song was finished, the audience <u>clapped</u>.

Ⓑ I will <u>mark</u> this page.

Ⓒ She is very <u>wealthy</u>.

Ⓓ no mistake

 4

Ⓕ Daniel did not <u>recieve</u> my letter.

Ⓖ He hurt his <u>wrist</u>.

Ⓗ I have a new <u>suit</u>.

Ⓙ no mistake

54

Name _____

Use the table of contents to choose the correct answer to each question.

```
TABLE OF CONTENTS
                                    Page
Helen, the Pelican. . . . . . . . . . . . . . . . . . . 5
The Elephant's Trunk . . . . . . . . . . . . . . 15
Baboon Families. . . . . . . . . . . . . . . . . . 21
Fishy Tales . . . . . . . . . . . . . . . . . . . . . . 30
```

1 **Which is the longest story?**

Ⓐ "Helen, the Pelican"

Ⓑ "Baboon Families"

Ⓒ "The Elephant's Trunk"

2 **On which page would you begin to read "Fishy Tales"?**

Ⓕ 21

Ⓖ 30

Ⓗ 31

3 **The stories in this book are probably about —**

Ⓐ many kinds of fish.

Ⓑ many kinds of animals.

Ⓒ many kinds of families.

4 **On which page would you look to find a story about elephants?**

Ⓕ 5

Ⓖ 15

Ⓗ 21

55

Name _____

For each item below, choose the word that *means the same or almost the same* (synonym) as the <u>underlined word</u>.

❶ to <u>trade</u> is to —

Ⓐ earn
Ⓑ tired
Ⓒ swap
Ⓓ trouble

❷ <u>everybody</u> means —

Ⓕ even
Ⓖ all
Ⓗ bodies
Ⓙ ever

❸ a <u>gift</u> is a —

Ⓐ general
Ⓑ give
Ⓒ present
Ⓓ toy

❹ to <u>stand</u> is to —

Ⓕ sit
Ⓖ stool
Ⓗ rise
Ⓙ grand

Name _____

Read each sentence and look at the <u>underlined words</u>. There may be a mistake in them. Select the best answer to correct the mistake. If there is no mistake, select *correct as is*.

1 <u>**John carried his**</u> **rod and reel.**

   Ⓐ John carry his
   Ⓑ John carrying his
   Ⓒ John cared his
   Ⓓ correct as is

2 **Your dog is** <u>**big than mine**</u>**.**

   Ⓕ most big than mine
   Ⓖ bigger than mine
   Ⓗ biggest than mine
   Ⓙ correct as is

3 **The manatee** <u>**is an animal**</u>**.**

   Ⓐ is a animal
   Ⓑ is am animal
   Ⓒ is and animal
   Ⓓ correct as is

4 <u>**They books are**</u> **too heavy.**

   Ⓕ Their books are
   Ⓖ There books are
   Ⓗ Them books are
   Ⓙ correct as is

57

Name _____

Fill in the bubble next to the correct way to punctuate the <u>underlined words</u>. If there is no mistake, choose *correct as is*.

---

1 At our graduation ceremony, the president of our class sang "<u>The Future is in Our Hands</u>."

  Ⓐ <u>The Future is in Our Hands</u>

  Ⓑ *The Future is in Our Hands*

  Ⓒ correct as is

---

2 My grandparents sent us a subscription to "<u>National Environment</u>" magazine that we get once a month.

  Ⓕ *National Environment*

  Ⓖ National Environment

  Ⓗ correct as is

---

3 Hiro wrote a poem called <u>The Man Without a Name</u>.

  Ⓐ The Man Without a Name

  Ⓑ "The Man Without a Name"

  Ⓒ correct as is

---

4 Armen finished reading the third chapter of <u>Tales of the Fourth Grade Blues</u> by Judy Frost.

  Ⓕ "Tales of the Fourth Grade Blues"

  Ⓖ Tales of the Fourth Grade Blues

  Ⓗ correct as is

Name _____

Students in Mrs. William's class were asked to write a report about animals. Luis decided to write about how some animals migrate. Luis went to the library to get information on the migration of the blue whale.

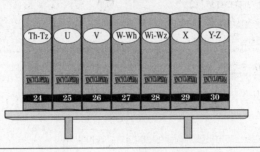

1 What volume of the encyclopedia should Luis look in to get started?

Ⓐ 24

Ⓑ 26

Ⓒ 27

Ⓓ 28

2 Which set of guide words would tell the page where Luis should look to learn about whales?

Ⓕ wallet — waves

Ⓖ weather — whistle

Ⓗ whistle — wind

Ⓙ window — wrap

59

Luis continued to research the migration of the blue whale for his report. He visited his local library and went online to find more information. Use the information below to answer the questions on the following page.

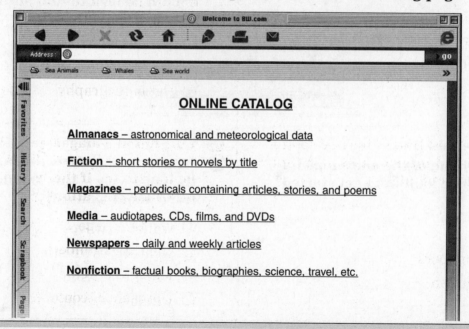

1 Which source from the online catalog should Luis use to find books about whales and their migration patterns?

Ⓐ almanacs

Ⓑ fiction

Ⓒ newspapers

Ⓓ nonfiction

2 If Luis would like to look at some audio-visual information, what source should he look at?

Ⓕ magazines

Ⓖ media

Ⓗ newspapers

Ⓙ nonfiction

3 Luis found a book that might have some information on whales and their migration. Where in the book should he look to find out if this information is there?

Ⓐ the index   Ⓒ the footnotes

Ⓑ the bibliography   Ⓓ the title page

4 Luis found a magazine called *Science and Nature*. Where should he look to see if there is an article on whale migration?

Ⓕ the title page

Ⓖ the page numbers

Ⓗ the references

Ⓙ the table of contents

61

Name _____

**I had a turkey sandwich for lunch.
I had an apple for lunch.**

How can these sentences be
combined without changing the
meaning?

Ⓐ I had a turkey and apple
    sandwich for lunch.

Ⓑ I had a turkey sandwich, but not
    an apple for lunch.

Ⓒ For lunch I had a turkey
    sandwich and an apple.

**James went to the park. Danny did
not go to the park.**

How can these sentences be
combined without changing the
meaning?

Ⓕ James and Danny went to the
    park.

Ⓖ James went to the park, but
    Danny did not.

Ⓗ Danny went to the park without
    James.

62

Name _____

For each number below, choose the word(s) that will make a *telling sentence* (statement).

❶ _____ **been raining all day.**

Ⓐ It
Ⓑ Has it
Ⓒ It has

❸ _____ **doing their homework.**

Ⓐ The girls were
Ⓑ Were the girls
Ⓒ Girls were the

❷ _____ **working for many hours.**

Ⓕ Have they been
Ⓖ Been have they
Ⓗ They have been

❹ _____ **to the bank.**

Ⓕ Is Mother going
Ⓖ Mother is going
Ⓗ Going is Mother

63

Name _____

Fill in the bubble next to the word that correctly completes each sentence.

❶ **The trainer rode on the back of ____ whale.**

Ⓐ a

Ⓑ an

❷ **____ abacus was used for counting.**

Ⓕ A

Ⓖ An

❸ **Lorenzo bought ____ two-scoop ice-cream cone.**

Ⓐ a

Ⓑ an

❹ **The carpenter cut ____ opening in the wall.**

Ⓕ a

Ⓖ an

Name _____

Fill in the bubble next to the prefix that correctly completes each sentence.

1 I'm sorry you were ____informed.

- Ⓐ re-
- Ⓑ dis-
- Ⓒ mis-
- Ⓓ in-

2 Her grades should ___prove with tutoring.

- Ⓕ in-
- Ⓖ im-
- Ⓗ un-
- Ⓙ en-

3 The workmen will ___stripe the street.

- Ⓐ re-
- Ⓑ ex-
- Ⓒ dis-
- Ⓓ in-

4 Their meeting seemed to be ____planned.

- Ⓕ dis-
- Ⓖ un-
- Ⓗ en-
- Ⓙ ex-

65

Read the passage below. Then answer the questions on the next page. You may look back at this page as you answer the questions.

Pizza is often thought of as being Italian. But pizza can be made by anyone using almost any kind of food on any kind of crust.

The crust can be made "from scratch" by mixing, rolling, and then baking all of the ingredients. You will need flour, shortening, yeast, sugar, and salt. Or you can use French bread, pita pocket bread, English muffins, or even tortillas for a crust.

The topping <u>usually</u> has cheese and a tomato sauce seasoned with herbs and spices. You can use small pieces of meat, or make a vegetable pizza, or a cold fruit pizza. Dessert pizza is made on a cookie crust.

Only one thing remains the same; pizza must have a crust to hold the topping.

Name _____

❶ From this passage you can tell that —

Ⓐ pizza can be made with different kinds of foods.

Ⓑ dessert pizza came from Italy.

Ⓒ pizza crust is always made "from scratch."

❷ <u>Usually</u> means —

Ⓕ us all.

Ⓖ seasoned.

Ⓗ often.

❸ A pizza has two main parts:

Ⓐ the shortening and the yeast.

Ⓑ the cheese and the tomato sauce.

Ⓒ the crust and the topping.

Ⓓ the meat and the vegetables.

❹ Number the steps to make pizza dough "from scratch."

___ baking

___ rolling

___ mixing

Name _____

Fill in the bubble next to the answer that is punctuated correctly.

1 **Did you see the —**

Ⓐ rainbow?

Ⓑ rainbow,

Ⓒ rainbow.

Ⓓ rain'bow

2 _____ **be home before midnight.**

Ⓕ Well

Ⓖ Well'

Ⓗ We'll

Ⓙ Wel'l

3 **Many travelers visit —**

Ⓐ Cooperstown New York.

Ⓑ Cooperstown New, York.

Ⓒ Cooperstown, New York?

Ⓓ Cooperstown, New York.

4 **Have you read —**

Ⓕ *The Adventures of Liam Sorrento.*

Ⓖ *The Adventures of Liam Sorrento?*

Ⓗ *The Adventures of Liam Sorrento,*

Ⓙ *The Adventures of Liam Sorrento!*

Name _____

Read each sentence and look at the <u>underlined words</u>. There may be a mistake in them. Select the best answer to correct the mistake. If there is no mistake, select *correct as is*.

❶ <u>Dad started</u> a new job today.

    Ⓐ Dad start
    Ⓑ Dad starting
    Ⓒ Dad have started
    Ⓓ correct as is

❷ <u>I sawing that show</u> on TV.

    Ⓕ I seen that show
    Ⓖ I have saw that show
    Ⓗ I saw that show
    Ⓙ correct as is

❸ The <u>book were open</u> on the desk.

    Ⓐ book is open
    Ⓑ book be open
    Ⓒ book am open
    Ⓓ correct as is

❹ The <u>cup be full</u>.

    Ⓕ cup are full
    Ⓖ cup were full
    Ⓗ cup was full
    Ⓙ correct as is

69

Name _____

In each group, fill in the bubble in front of the word that could be the *main heading* for the other three words.

❶

Ⓐ soccer
Ⓑ baseball
Ⓒ sport
Ⓓ basketball

❷

Ⓕ pine
Ⓖ oak
Ⓗ walnut
Ⓙ wood

❸

Ⓐ vehicle
Ⓑ van
Ⓒ car
Ⓓ truck

❹

Ⓕ red
Ⓖ color
Ⓗ blue
Ⓙ green

Name _____

Mark the bubble next to the sentence that goes *best* on the blank line in each paragraph.

❶   **It was time to plant our garden. _____**
In the summertime, we'll have lots of different kinds of vegetables.

Ⓐ Our soil was ready.

Ⓑ We bought three tomato plants.

Ⓒ We planted peas, beans, corn, tomatoes, and cucumbers.

_____

❷   **_____ He cleaned my teeth**
and filled one of hers. He told us to come back next year.

Ⓕ Ahmad and Aisha are twins.

Ⓖ Mother and I went to the dentist.

Ⓗ We will go again another time.

BELLWORK Reading/Language Arts • Level 4

Name _____

Fill in the bubble next to the sentence that is capitalized correctly.

1
- Ⓐ My brother attends Warren High School.
- Ⓑ My brother attends Warren high School.
- Ⓒ My brother attends Warren high school.

2
- Ⓕ The Eiffel Tower is in paris, france.
- Ⓖ The Eiffel Tower is in paris, France.
- Ⓗ The Eiffel Tower is in Paris, France.

3
- Ⓐ John Adams was president of the United states.
- Ⓑ John Adams was President of the United States.
- Ⓒ John Adams was president of the united states.

4
- Ⓕ The movie was made in los Angeles.
- Ⓖ The movie was made in Los Angeles.
- Ⓗ The movie was made in Los angeles.

Name _____

Look carefully at each group of words. Then choose the compound word (two words put together).

1
- Ⓐ hardly
- Ⓑ sometime
- Ⓒ careful
- Ⓓ sunny

2
- Ⓕ soldier
- Ⓖ closet
- Ⓗ handy
- Ⓙ toothpaste

3
- Ⓐ everyone
- Ⓑ pencil
- Ⓒ fasten
- Ⓓ replace

4
- Ⓕ colorful
- Ⓖ sickness
- Ⓗ firewood
- Ⓙ printer

Name _____

Fill in the bubble next to the word that correctly completes each sentence.

1 The _____ turned out great.

Ⓐ picturies
Ⓑ picture's
Ⓒ pictures
Ⓓ picturess

2 The _____ are growing fast.

Ⓕ child
Ⓖ children
Ⓗ childs
Ⓙ childrens

3 There are six _____ at the park.

Ⓐ family
Ⓑ familys
Ⓒ familie
Ⓓ families

4 We travel three _____ to school.

Ⓕ mile
Ⓖ milles
Ⓗ mileses
Ⓙ miles

Name _____

Read the two sentences. Fill in the bubble next to the word that makes sense in *both* sentences.

1 Our class went to see a good _____ in the auditorium.

We like to _____ soccer.

Ⓐ drama
Ⓑ movie
Ⓒ play
Ⓓ watch

2 They dug a _____ in the backyard.

He felt very _____ this morning.

Ⓕ healthy
Ⓖ hole
Ⓗ tired
Ⓙ well

3 Mother _____ the new baby, Anthony.

Yesterday, I _____ my mother at her job.

Ⓐ talked
Ⓑ called
Ⓒ phoned
Ⓓ named

4 The painting is a _____ of art.

The teacher said I need to _____ on my math skills.

Ⓕ work
Ⓖ toil
Ⓗ job
Ⓙ product

75

Read the passage below. Then answer the question on the next page. You may look back at this page as you answer the question.

More than two hundred species of turtles live in deserts, forests, grasslands, lakes, rivers, ponds, marshes, and the oceans. Some have stumpy legs. Others have webbed feet or flapper-like paddles to help them swim. Some live on land and in water.

Tortoises are turtles that live only on land. Like bears, they hibernate in the winter. When it gets cold, they dig a hole in the ground and stay there until the weather gets warm again in the springtime.

Some turtles live all their lives near where they were hatched; others swim thousands of miles away. Turtles may be only three to five inches long. Other kinds grow to be four to eight feet long. Some are speedy; some are slow. Some have hard shells; others' shells are soft.

Since turtles and tortoises have no teeth, you might think they would have a hard time eating, but with their hard beaks and strong jaws, they can eat the toughest foods.

Name _____

Look at the story web below. It shows some of the facts about turtles. One of the boxes is empty. Find another fact about turtles.

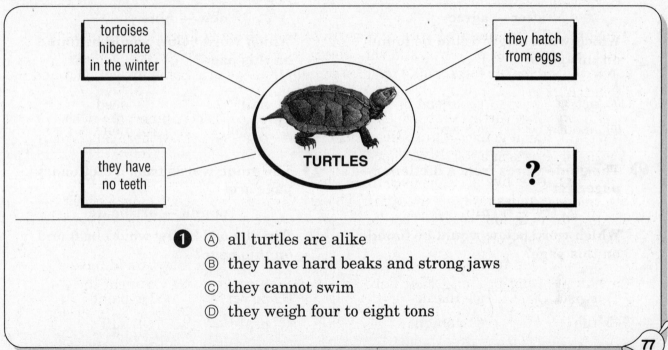

1 Ⓐ all turtles are alike
   Ⓑ they have hard beaks and strong jaws
   Ⓒ they cannot swim
   Ⓓ they weigh four to eight tons

BELLWORK Reading/Language Arts • Level 4

Name _____

1 **The guide words from a dictionary page are:**

after — agree

Which word below would be found on this page?

Ⓐ act   Ⓒ ahead

Ⓑ about   Ⓓ age

2 **The guide words from a dictionary page are:**

try — turnip

Which word below would be found on this page?

Ⓕ twist   Ⓗ thank

Ⓖ tub   Ⓙ tonight

3 **The guide words from a dictionary page are:**

new — nine

Which word below would be found on this page?

Ⓐ nail   Ⓒ need

Ⓑ nickel   Ⓓ none

4 **The guide words from a dictionary page are:**

pound — predicate

Which word below would be found on this page?

Ⓕ power   Ⓗ paint

Ⓖ peal   Ⓙ puff

78

Name _____

This is an entry from a thesaurus.

rugged, *adj.*

1. coarse, rough
2. stormy, violent, wild
3. strenuous, tough
4. hard-bitten

 The <u>rugged</u> hurricane blew across the state and tore up everything in sight.

Which numbered line from the thesaurus gives the meaning of the word <u>rugged</u> as it is used in the sentence above?

Ⓐ 1

Ⓑ 2

Ⓒ 3

Ⓓ 4

Name _____

Fill in the bubble next to the words that make up the <u>underlined contraction</u> in each sentence.

1 <u>I've</u> been there before.

   Ⓐ I have
   Ⓑ I had
   Ⓒ I would
   Ⓓ I gave

2 I told her <u>you're</u> still my best friend.

   Ⓕ you will
   Ⓖ you are
   Ⓗ you here
   Ⓙ are you

3 <u>He'd</u> better watch out!

   Ⓐ He has
   Ⓑ He did
   Ⓒ He does
   Ⓓ He had

4 <u>Don't</u> forget your jacket.

   Ⓕ Don out
   Ⓖ Do not
   Ⓗ Did not
   Ⓙ I will

Name _____

❶ Which of these book titles comes *first* in alphabetical order?

Ⓐ <u>The Boy From Mars</u>
Ⓑ <u>Timmy's Terrible Tuesday</u>
Ⓒ <u>A Girl Named Amanda</u>

❷ Which of these President's names comes *last* in alphabetical order?

Ⓕ Abraham Lincoln
Ⓖ George Washington
Ⓗ George Bush

❸ Which of these people's names comes *second* in alphabetical order?

Ⓐ Sarah Thomson
Ⓑ William Perry
Ⓒ Allison Smith

❹ Which of these cities comes *last* in alphabetical order?

Ⓕ Atlanta
Ⓖ Austin
Ⓗ Anaheim

81

Name _____

Fill in the bubble next to the correct answer.

1 **Where in a book is the *index* found?**

Ⓐ on the title page

Ⓑ in the front

Ⓒ at the back

Ⓓ on the cover

2 **It is easier to find the exact page on which a topic is covered in the —**

Ⓕ glossary.

Ⓖ table of contents.

Ⓗ index.

3 **An *index* tells —**

Ⓐ page numbers where topics are found.

Ⓑ who wrote the book.

Ⓒ how many pages are in the book.

Ⓓ the names of the chapters.

4 **Which marking below shows that information continues for several pages in a row (next to each other)?**

Ⓕ 1, 3, 44

Ⓖ 1-3

Name _____

Read each set of sentences and decide if one of the <u>underlined words</u> is spelled incorrectly, or if there is *no mistake*. Choose your answer and fill in the bubble.

1

Ⓐ He puts <u>honey</u> in his tea.

Ⓑ All the children were <u>hidin</u> from Grace.

Ⓒ We should have a <u>debate</u>.

Ⓓ no mistake

2

Ⓕ We landed on <u>solid</u> ground.

Ⓖ I will <u>accept</u> your offer.

Ⓗ Marianne went <u>joging</u> with her mother.

Ⓙ no mistake

3

Ⓐ Do you <u>believe</u> what he says?

Ⓑ There is no <u>difference</u>.

Ⓒ Are you <u>buying</u> that?

Ⓓ no mistake

4

Ⓕ Sam <u>passed</u> the football to Thomas.

Ⓖ Three <u>familys</u> went to the game together.

Ⓗ Don't touch those <u>controls</u>!

Ⓙ no mistake

83

Read both passages below. Then answer the questions on the next page. You may look back at this page as you answer the questions.

Sample A

A New York City Tradition

New Year's Eve is a spectacular event in Times Square in New York City. The evening is full of sights, sounds, and special effects featuring the tradition of the Ball Lowering in Times Square. Thousands of people come to watch this special event. Atop a flagpole at 1 Times Square, the ball is lowered at exactly midnight. Although the first Times Square New Year's Eve celebration was held in 1904, the first ball was lowered in 1907 and has been a tradition ever since. The Ball Lowering in Times Square has become a universal symbol of welcoming in the New Year.

Sample B

January 2, 1999

What a night to remember! My parents took my brother and me to New York for our winter break at school. We were staying through New Year's to watch all of the excitement taking place in the city. We got to Times Square very early on New Year's Eve. They were going to be blocking the streets off because of all of the celebrations. There were people everywhere. Everyone was bundled up to fight the cold weather. Everyone was in a great mood and ready to celebrate the New Year. Right before midnight, people started the countdown; 10, 9, 8, 7...and finally we all shouted out, "Happy New Year." At exactly midnight the beautifully lit ball was lowered from the flagpole. We all cheered. What an amazing and unforgettable New Year!

Name _____

Fill in the bubble next to the answer that correctly completes each sentence.

1 **Information from _both_ samples tells that —**

Ⓐ the Ball Lowering has been a tradition since 1907.

Ⓑ the flagpole is at 1 Times Square.

Ⓒ at exactly midnight the ball is lowered.

2 **You can tell from the title of Sample A that the author is going to —**

Ⓕ persuade you to move somewhere.

Ⓖ describe an event.

Ⓗ teach you to make something.

3 **What would you need to add to Sample B's journal entry to make it a letter?**

Ⓐ pictures

Ⓑ a greeting and a closing

Ⓒ a reference to a book

4 Sentence from Sample B

At exactly midnight the **beautifully** lit ball was lowered from the flagpole.

The root word of beautifully means —

Ⓕ generally pleasing.

Ⓖ unpleasant.

Ⓗ awkward or strange.

85

Name _____

Fill in the bubble next to the answer that is the root (base) of the <u>underlined word</u>.

1 **The root (base) of the word <u>flatten</u> is —**

Ⓐ flat.
Ⓑ flatt.
Ⓒ flatte.
Ⓓ ten.

2 **The root (base) of the word <u>answered</u> is —**

Ⓕ an.
Ⓖ were.
Ⓗ red.
Ⓙ answer.

3 **The root (base) of the word <u>carefully</u> is —**

Ⓐ car.
Ⓑ care.
Ⓒ careful.
Ⓓ fully.

4 **The root (base) of the word <u>hardly</u> is —**

Ⓕ heard.
Ⓖ hardy.
Ⓗ hard.
Ⓙ ardly.

86

Name _____

Fill in the bubble next to the words needed to form a *question*.

❶ _____ hot dogs?

Ⓐ Like you do
Ⓑ Do you like
Ⓒ You do like
Ⓓ Do you

❷ _____ to play dodgeball?

Ⓕ You are going
Ⓖ Going, are you
Ⓗ Are you going
Ⓙ Hey, you are

Fill in the bubble next to the words needed to form a *statement*.

❸ Haley's doll _____.

Ⓐ has lost an arm
Ⓑ have lost an arm
Ⓒ has arm lost
Ⓓ losed an arm

❹ _____ to raise that puppy.

Ⓕ Will Bob be able
Ⓖ Had Bob be able
Ⓗ Bob will be able
Ⓙ Able Bob will be

87

Read the passage below. Then answer the questions on the next page. You may look back at this page as you answer the questions.

WALKING SHOES

For Men and Women, Dress and Casual Shoes
for the entire family

RUNNING SHOES, BASEBALL SHOES,

GOLF AND COURT SHOES....

WE HAVE THEM ALL!!

We GUARANTEE

to beat the price at any other store or your money back!

Come in today for the

BEST SHOES at the BEST PRICE.

Name _____

1 **Choose the *author's purpose*.**

Ⓐ to entertain
Ⓑ to teach
Ⓒ to sell
Ⓓ to buy

2 **The word <u>guarantee</u> means —**

Ⓕ promise.
Ⓖ quart.
Ⓗ T-shirt.
Ⓙ hope.

3 **The passage says that —**

Ⓐ all the shoes are free.
Ⓑ they have the best prices.
Ⓒ they like to sell shoes.
Ⓓ they sell boots.

4 **This passage is *mostly* about —**

Ⓕ men's walking shoes.
Ⓖ court shoes.
Ⓗ many kinds of shoes.
Ⓙ running shoes.

89

Name _____

Fill in the bubble next to the word that correctly completes each sentence.

❶ Bjorn _____ a letter to his cousin.

Ⓐ wrote

Ⓑ writed

Ⓒ writing

Ⓓ written

❷ The sailor _____ on the deck.

Ⓕ standed

Ⓖ standing

Ⓗ stood

Ⓙ stand

❸ Our class _____ the prize.

Ⓐ win

Ⓑ winning

Ⓒ won

Ⓓ woned

❹ Mama _____ me a dollar for lunch.

Ⓕ has gave

Ⓖ gived

Ⓗ gave

Ⓙ giving

Name _____

Read each sentence and look at the underlined word(s). There may be a mistake in them.
Select the best answer to correct the mistake. If there is no mistake, select *correct as is*.

1 **W. C. Fields** was a well-known actor.

Ⓐ w c Fields
Ⓑ W c Fields
Ⓒ w. c. Fields
Ⓓ correct as is

2 **They polished thair** white shoes.

Ⓕ They polished there
Ⓖ They polished their
Ⓗ They polished they're
Ⓙ correct as is

3 **Mother has did** the baking for the sale.

Ⓐ Mother do
Ⓑ Mother did
Ⓒ Mother done
Ⓓ correct as is

4 I hope you will not **disunderstand** the directions.

Ⓕ ununderstand
Ⓖ reunderstand
Ⓗ misunderstand
Ⓙ correct as is

Name _____

The dog was sleeping.
It was sleeping by the fire.

How can these sentences be combined without changing the meaning?

Ⓐ The sleeping fire was by the dog.

Ⓑ The dog was sleeping by the fire.

Ⓒ The dog was on fire.

Ⓓ The dog was by the fire, and not sleeping.

The girl was crying.
The girl was in her room.

How can these sentences be combined without changing the meaning?

Ⓕ The girl was crying beside her room.

Ⓖ The girl was in her room, but not crying.

Ⓗ The girl wasn't crying in her room.

Ⓙ The girl was crying in her room.

Name _____

Mr. Switzer's class is studying Native Americans. He asked each of his students to choose a group of Native Americans and write a report about them. Kinzi decided to write about the Navajos. She went to the library to look for information on the Navajos.

❶ While typing her report on the computer, Kinzi made a mistake. To erase the word, what should she do?

Ⓐ highlight the word and press Enter

Ⓑ skip the word and hope no one notices

Ⓒ highlight the word and press Delete

Ⓓ press Ctrl, Alt, and Delete altogether at the same time

❷ If Kinzi is going to quote information from a book in her report, she should cite all of these except what?

Ⓕ the author

Ⓖ the publisher

Ⓗ her teacher

Ⓙ the page number

93

This is the first draft of Kinzi's report. Read it and answer the questions on the following page.

Navajo Indians

1   The largest tribe of North American Indians is the Navajo. The Dine Indians, as they called themselves, had ancestors that lived in northwestern Canada and Alaska. Over a thousand years ago, they began to travel South and reached the southwestern United States. The Navajo have used resources from the land and other people to become the largest Native American reservation in the United States.

2   The Navajo Indians used the resources from the land to build their homes using wooden poles, tree bark, and mud. Their homes were called "hogans."

3   They met the Pueblo Indians, whom they settled near, and learned farming skills. They learned how to plant corn or "maize" and beans, squash, and melons. They also learned how to weave to make clothing and artwork.

4   In the 1600s after the Spanish had settled, the Navajo Indians got sheep and horses from them so they could also use their resources. They got wool from the sheep for clothing, blankets, and rugs. They also used the sheep for food. They used the horses to travel long distances, and traded them for supplies that they might need.

5   The Navajo began making pottery and blankets. They traded these items in town and at trading posts on the reservation. Today, the reservation has over 140,000 Navajo, with 16 million acres of land mostly in Arizona. They still use many of the resources available to them.

Name _____

1 **What would be the best topic sentence to add to the report?**

Ⓐ Navajo Indians have lived a long time.

Ⓑ Navajo Indians are resourceful people.

Ⓒ Navajo Indians have lived in many places.

Ⓓ Navajo Indians are intelligent and kind.

2 **When rewriting her report, Kinzi uses a thesaurus to look up the word "resource." What is she trying to find out?**

Ⓕ an antonym for resource

Ⓖ how to spell resource

Ⓗ a synonym for resource

Ⓙ different kinds of resources

3 **If Kinzi is trying to add more information to her report, besides that which she finds online, in what other resource might she look?**

Ⓐ dictionary

Ⓑ thesaurus

Ⓒ almanac

Ⓓ encyclopedia

4 **After typing her report on the computer, Kinzi should save her work on the —**

Ⓕ software.

Ⓖ soft drive.

Ⓗ hardware.

Ⓙ hard drive.

95

Name _____

Fill in the bubble next to the *best* source of information.

❶ To find a list of all the books about earthquakes, look in —

- Ⓐ a newspaper.
- Ⓑ a telephone directory.
- Ⓒ a library's computer.
- Ⓓ an atlas.

❷ To find a list of words with similar meanings, look in —

- Ⓕ an almanac.
- Ⓖ a newspaper.
- Ⓗ an atlas.
- Ⓙ a thesaurus.

❸ To find a map showing the Amazon River, look in —

- Ⓐ an almanac.
- Ⓑ a dictionary.
- Ⓒ a glossary.
- Ⓓ an atlas.

❹ To find the time of low tide, look in —

- Ⓕ a dictionary.
- Ⓖ an almanac.
- Ⓗ a table of contents.
- Ⓙ an index.

96

Name _____

Read each sentence and look at the <u>underlined words</u>. There may be a mistake in them. Select the best answer to correct the mistake. If there is no mistake, select *correct as is*.

❶ Our room mother is <u>Mrs. Smith.</u>

    Ⓐ Mrs Smith.

    Ⓑ Mrs, Smith.

    Ⓒ Mrs" Smith.

    Ⓓ correct as is

❷ We had <u>hamburgers. hot dogs,</u> and potato chips.

    Ⓕ hamburgers hot dogs,

    Ⓖ hamburgers, hot dogs,

    Ⓗ hamburgers; hot dogs,

    Ⓙ correct as is

❸ Christmas is always on <u>Dec, 25.</u>

    Ⓐ Dec 25.

    Ⓑ Dec' 25.

    Ⓒ Dec. 25.

    Ⓓ correct as is

❹ The <u>flag of the U.S.A</u> is red, white, and blue.

    Ⓕ flag of the U.S.A.

    Ⓖ flag of the USA

    Ⓗ flag of the U,S,A.

    Ⓙ correct as is

97

Name _____

Fill in the bubble next to the part of speech that identifies the <u>underlined word</u>.

1 Yi-rang <u>walked</u> to the park after school.

Ⓐ verb
Ⓑ adverb
Ⓒ preposition
Ⓓ conjunction

2 The frog jumped <u>quickly</u> across the lily pads.

Ⓕ verb
Ⓖ adverb
Ⓗ preposition
Ⓙ conjunction

3 Marcus was reading <u>in</u> the library.

Ⓐ verb
Ⓑ adverb
Ⓒ preposition
Ⓓ conjunction

4 Brandon rode his bike to Eric's house <u>and</u> played basketball.

Ⓕ verb
Ⓖ adverb
Ⓗ preposition
Ⓙ conjunction

Name _____

Read the poem. Fill in the bubble by your answer. Then follow the written instruction below.

> "Rain, rain, go away.
> Come again some other day.
> Little Johnny wants to play."

❶ Exactly how does little Johnny feel about the rain?

Ⓐ He likes it.

Ⓑ He wants more rain.

Ⓒ He wishes it would not rain today.

❷ Write a few words on the lines below to tell how *you* feel about the rain.

_____

_____

_____

99

Name _____

 His temper was as explosive as a volcano.

This is an example of a —

Ⓐ hyperbole.

Ⓑ simile.

 The older couple was drowning in money.

This is an example of a —

Ⓕ metaphor.

Ⓖ personification.

 Joey ate a mile-high ice-cream cone.

This is an example of a —

Ⓐ simile.

Ⓑ hyperbole.

 The tropical storm slept for two days.

This is an example of a —

Ⓕ metaphor.

Ⓖ personification.

Name _____

Fill in the bubble next to the sentence that is capitalized correctly.

1
Ⓐ Peter Tchaikovsky wrote the song "Dance of the Sugarplum Fairies."

Ⓑ Peter Tchaikovsky wrote the Song "dance of the Sugarplum Fairies."

Ⓒ Peter Tchaikovsky wrote the Song "Dance of the sugarplum fairies."

2
Ⓕ My grandmother does the crossword puzzle from our local Newspaper.

Ⓖ My grandmother does the crossword puzzle from our local newspaper.

Ⓗ My grandmother does the Crossword Puzzle from our local newspaper.

3
Ⓐ The Hapshaw County tribune gets delivered to our door every day.

Ⓑ The Hapshaw County Tribune gets delivered to our door every day.

Ⓒ The hapshaw county Tribune gets delivered to our door every day.

4
Ⓕ Veronika is a volunteer for the Library of Congress.

Ⓖ Veronika is a Volunteer for the Library of congress.

Ⓗ Veronika is a Volunteer for the library of congress.

101

Name _____

Fill in the bubble in front of the word(s) that best complete each sentence correctly.

1 John makes _____ grades than Bill.

Ⓐ good
Ⓑ better
Ⓒ best
Ⓓ gooder

2 Jill is _____ than her sisters.

Ⓕ younger
Ⓖ most youngest
Ⓗ young
Ⓙ youngest

3 Mike is the _____ boy in the class.

Ⓐ tall
Ⓑ taller
Ⓒ tallest
Ⓓ most tall

4 That's the _____ story I've ever heard!

Ⓕ funny
Ⓖ funnest
Ⓗ funnier
Ⓙ funniest

Name _____

Fill in the bubble in front of the answer that tells the *author's purpose*.

1 Fuzzy Wuzzy was a bear. Fuzzy Wuzzy had no hair. Fuzzy Wuzzy wasn't fuzzy, was he?

Ⓐ to inform
Ⓑ to teach
Ⓒ to entertain
Ⓓ to persuade

2 We have the best computers you can buy at the best prices anywhere. Come in today. Let us help you choose the system that suits your needs.

Ⓕ to inform   Ⓗ to persuade
Ⓖ to entertain   Ⓙ to teach

3 Many people believe that vitamin C can be helpful in preventing colds, and even cancer and heart attacks. You can get vitamin C from oranges, tangerines, grapefruit, and tomatoes, or in pill form.

Ⓐ to inform   Ⓒ to persuade
Ⓑ to entertain   Ⓓ to invite

4 25 x 2 = 50

Ⓕ to invite
Ⓖ to entertain
Ⓗ to persuade
Ⓙ to teach

103

Read the passage below. Then answer the questions on the next page. You may look back at this page as you answer the questions.

The long, thin, grassy leaves of the spider plant look something like the legs of a spider. It is usually planted in a hanging basket to make room for the new little "spiders" that grow at the ends of long slender stems. The spider plant is easy to grow inside as a houseplant or outdoors in warm places. Sometimes there are so many leaves, stems, and little plants that it looks like a web with many spiders on it.

Each new plant already has roots. To make a new plant grow, all you have to do is cut the little one off, pot it in good soil, and keep it moist and warm. Soon you'll have many more little spiders hanging from the one you planted.

Some people use spider plants as <u>ground cover</u>. They put the plants in the ground outdoors. The little spiders take root right where they are, and soon the ground is covered with spider plants.

1 **The spider plant got its name because —**

Ⓐ it can move from place to place.

Ⓑ it looks like a spider.

Ⓒ it can spin a web.

2 **Spider plants can grow —**

Ⓕ indoors only.

Ⓖ outside only.

Ⓗ inside and outdoors.

3 **A spider plant can —**

Ⓐ produce new plants.

Ⓑ sting you.

Ⓒ hang a basket.

4 **In this passage ground cover means —**

Ⓕ to grind up clover.

Ⓖ to cover the ground.

Ⓗ to plant grass.

105

Name _____

Read each sentence. Fill in the bubble next to the word(s) needed to form a complete sentence.

1 The beaver _____ to build his dam.

   Ⓐ slowly
   Ⓑ a lot of bark
   Ⓒ uses tree branches
   Ⓓ his tail on the water

2 Potato chips _____.

   Ⓕ are crunchy
   Ⓖ at the store
   Ⓗ salty
   Ⓙ taste

3 The house _____.

   Ⓐ on the hill
   Ⓑ needs paint
   Ⓒ for sale
   Ⓓ was not

4 She _____ to the mailbox.

   Ⓕ a letter
   Ⓖ took a letter
   Ⓗ a local newspaper
   Ⓙ a heavy package

Name _____

Choose the correct capitalization and punctuation needed in the sentences below.

His name was _____1_____ **, and he worked for** _____2_____

1 Ⓐ a j. Manken

   Ⓑ a. j. Manken

   Ⓒ A. j. Manken

   Ⓓ A. J. Manken

2 Ⓕ Standard Civil Engineering Co.

   Ⓖ standard Civil Engineering Co.

   Ⓗ Standard civil Engineering Co.

   Ⓙ Standard Civil Engineering co.

The company's address is _____3_____ **in** _____4_____

3 Ⓐ 1234 Arcadia Place

   Ⓑ 1234 arcadia place

   Ⓒ 1234 Arcadia place

   Ⓓ 1234 arcadia Place

4 Ⓕ bend oregon.

   Ⓖ Bend oregon.

   Ⓗ Bend, Oregon.

   Ⓙ bend, Oregon.

107

Name _____

Use the table of contents to choose the correct answer to each question.

TABLE OF CONTENTS

1 On what page would you find "California Missions"?

Ⓐ 16   Ⓒ 22

Ⓑ 8   Ⓓ 5

2 On what page does "Farming in the Central Valley" begin?

Ⓕ 5   Ⓗ 16

Ⓖ 8   Ⓙ 22

3 Most of the stories in this book are probably about —

Ⓐ farming.   Ⓒ missions.

Ⓑ beaches.   Ⓓ California.

4 What would you be reading about if you were on page 20?

Ⓕ beaches   Ⓗ the state capital

Ⓖ missions   Ⓙ farming

Name _____

Read each sentence and look at the <u>underlined words</u>. There may be a mistake in them.
Select the best answer to correct the mistake. If there is no mistake, select *correct as is*.

❶ <u>Her had</u> a cold but went to school anyway.

Ⓐ Them had

Ⓑ Him had

Ⓒ She had

Ⓓ correct as is

❷ <u>Cody and me</u> like to skate on the sidewalk.

Ⓕ Cody and I

Ⓖ Cody and them

Ⓗ Cody and us

Ⓙ correct as is

❸ That colored <u>pencil is my</u>!

Ⓐ pencil is me's

Ⓑ pencil is I

Ⓒ pencil is mine

Ⓓ correct as is

❹ The teacher <u>told we</u> to study quietly.

Ⓕ told I

Ⓖ told they

Ⓗ told us

Ⓙ correct as is

109

Read the passage below. Then answer the questions on the next page. You may look back at this page as you answer the questions.

How Giraffe Got a Long Neck

1 In the great Savanna grasslands there lived both predators and their prey. Lions and cheetahs roamed the hot grasslands while other animals protected themselves by standing in groups. Every animal had its own characteristics: Zebra had its stripes, Cheetah had its speed and spots, however, Giraffe seemed ordinary with no outstanding feature.

2 Now Giraffe used to have a very average size neck. He always admired Ostrich for his good looks and long neck. One day Giraffe found a wonderful acacia tree standing alone in the grasslands whose leaves had yet to be eaten. He stretched and stretched, but his average-sized neck just wouldn't let his hungry mouth reach the leaves.

3 Giraffe was very <u>discouraged</u> and went to talk to Ostrich. When he found Ostrich, he had his neck in a hole thinking he was hiding away from danger. Giraffe tried to talk to Ostrich about his own troubles, but Ostrich could not hear him with his head in the ground. Ostrich told him to put his head in the hole next to his so that they could talk.

4 After a long conversation, Giraffe tried to take his head back out of the hole, but it was stuck. Giraffe pulled and pulled. His neck began to stretch longer and longer, but it was still stuck. Ostrich stood behind him and tugged with all his might. Finally Giraffe's head came loose. Out came Giraffe, but in a different form. Giraffe's neck was longer than ever, even longer than Ostrich's. Giraffe was <u>ecstatic</u>. It was the perfect thing to make him unique and different and let him reach those wonderful acacia leaves that he was longing for. From that day on, all giraffes were born with long necks so they could reach the tall acacia leaves and have their own unique look!

110

Name _____

1 This passage is best described as a —

Ⓐ fantasy.

Ⓑ fable.

Ⓒ fairy tale.

Ⓓ legend.

2 After reading the fourth paragraph, the word <u>ecstatic</u> probably means —

Ⓕ very sticky.

Ⓖ very sad.

Ⓗ very confused.

Ⓙ very happy.

3 In the sentence "Giraffe was very discouraged and went to talk to Ostrich," the word <u>discouraged</u> means —

Ⓐ to have a lot of courage.

Ⓑ to take away courage.

Ⓒ to be brave.

4 The main purpose of the passage is to —

Ⓕ tell why something is a certain way.

Ⓖ describe different animals.

Ⓗ show the difference between predators and prey.

Ⓙ describe the grasslands.

111

Name _____

Mark the bubble next to the sentence which goes *best* on the blank line in each paragraph.

❶   **The farmer went to feed his cows. _____ , He looked in the barn but she was not there. He looked in the pasture but he could not see her. "I guess I'll have to go out in the rain to find her," he said.**

Ⓐ All of them were hungry.

Ⓑ He fed them every night and morning.

Ⓒ One of the cows was missing.

---

❷   **_____ It strengthens the legs and heart and helps the lungs take in more oxygen. A good brisk walk can improve the way you feel and help you to get a good night's sleep.**

Ⓕ Swimming is good exercise.

Ⓖ Walking is good for the body.

Ⓗ Get a good night's sleep.

Name _____

For each item below, choose the word that *means the same or almost the same* (synonym) as the underlined word.

---

❶ to ask is to —

Ⓐ and
Ⓑ as
Ⓒ invite
Ⓓ answer

❷ to touch is to —

Ⓕ feel
Ⓖ tone
Ⓗ trunk
Ⓙ tune

❸ to weep is to —

Ⓐ well
Ⓑ cry
Ⓒ crowd
Ⓓ weak

❹ to wish is to —

Ⓕ wash
Ⓖ want
Ⓗ fish
Ⓙ wise

Read the passage below. Then answer the question on the next page. You may look back at this page as you answer the question.

Did you know that forests can grow in the sea? Yes, off the coast of California there are forests of giant kelp, a kind of seaweed plant which grows to be fifty feet high, taller than many trees.

Kelp provides a home and protection for many kinds of creatures which live in the ocean. Crabs live in its "holdfast," root-like fibers that hold the kelp to rocks on the ocean floor. Schools of sardines and other small fish use the kelp to find protection from larger fish. Otters wrap themselves in the large leaves at the surface so they won't drift away when they go to sleep in a bed of kelp.

Some of the kelp is harvested by huge boats using conveyor belts to bring it aboard. Once on shore, it is processed into many products which we use every day, such as ice cream, mayonnaise, cosmetics, and fertilizer.

Name _____

Look at the web organizer below. It shows that kelp provides a home and protection for many creatures. Choose the phrase that *best* completes this web.

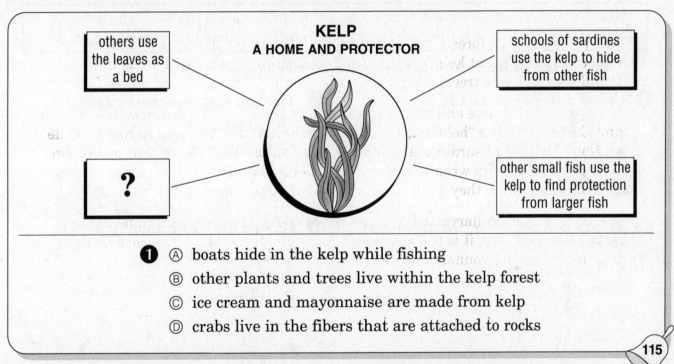

KELP
A HOME AND PROTECTOR

others use the leaves as a bed

schools of sardines use the kelp to hide from other fish

?

other small fish use the kelp to find protection from larger fish

1 Ⓐ boats hide in the kelp while fishing

Ⓑ other plants and trees live within the kelp forest

Ⓒ ice cream and mayonnaise are made from kelp

Ⓓ crabs live in the fibers that are attached to rocks

BELLWORK Reading/Language Arts • Level 4

Name _____

Use the dictionary entry and definitions to answer the question below.

---

box (boks) n. **1.** small section of seats in a theater or sports arena. **2.** a carton to hold things. v. **3.** to put things in a box. **4.** to fight another in a boxing match.

Which of the above meanings fits each sentence below?

---

❶ I need a large square <u>box</u>.

Ⓐ Definition 1
Ⓑ Definition 2
Ⓒ Definition 3
Ⓓ Definition 4

❷ Before moving, we <u>boxed</u> up a lot of things.

Ⓕ Definition 1
Ⓖ Definition 2
Ⓗ Definition 3
Ⓙ Definition 4

❸ The <u>box</u> seat was more expensive.

Ⓐ Definition 1
Ⓑ Definition 2
Ⓒ Definition 3
Ⓓ Definition 4

❹ My dad likes to watch fighters <u>box</u>.

Ⓕ Definition 1
Ⓖ Definition 2
Ⓗ Definition 3
Ⓙ Definition 4

116

Name _____

Read each numbered sentence, and look at the <u>underlined word</u>. Then choose the other sentence in which the <u>underlined word</u> is used in the same way.

1 She <u>broke</u> the law.

Ⓐ The ball <u>broke</u> the window.

Ⓑ She <u>broke</u> the record in the mile.

Ⓒ He <u>broke</u> a dollar bill into change.

Ⓓ They <u>broke</u> their promise.

2 Those samples are <u>free</u> of charge.

Ⓔ She was <u>free</u> to choose.

Ⓕ Buy two and get the third one <u>free</u>.

Ⓖ We let the bird go <u>free</u>.

Ⓗ The road is now <u>free</u> of rocks.

3 Don't <u>step</u> on the flowers!

Ⓐ Try to stay in <u>step</u> with the music.

Ⓑ This recipe has one critical <u>step</u>.

Ⓒ The stairs have ten <u>steps</u>.

Ⓓ Take one <u>step</u> backwards.

4 She cut the <u>tip</u> of her finger.

Ⓔ If you <u>tip</u> your glass, you will spill your milk.

Ⓕ They left the waitress a good <u>tip</u>.

Ⓖ We climbed to the <u>tip</u> of the mountain.

Ⓗ He gave me a great <u>tip</u> on golf.

117

Name _____

 Because there was a tornado, the house was torn to pieces.

The house being torn to pieces is an example of —

Ⓐ the cause of a tornado.
Ⓑ the effect of a tornado.
Ⓒ a fact about tornados.
Ⓓ an opinion about tornados.

 The little boy was playing with matches and started a fire.

The little boy was playing with matches is an example of —

Ⓕ the cause of a fire.
Ⓖ the effect of a fire.
Ⓗ a fact about fires.
Ⓙ an opinion about little boys.

 Kyle likes baseball. He thinks it is the best sport to play.

Kyle thinks the best sport to play is baseball is an example of —

Ⓐ the cause of baseball.
Ⓑ the effect of baseball.
Ⓒ a fact about baseball.
Ⓓ an opinion about baseball.

 Baby whales are called calves.

This is an example of —

Ⓕ the cause of whales having babies.
Ⓖ the effect of whales having babies.
Ⓗ a fact about whales.
Ⓙ an opinion about baby whales.

118

Name _____

① Emma's mom says "her eyes are bigger than her stomach." What does she mean?

- Ⓐ Emma thinks she can eat more than she can.
- Ⓑ Emma has the biggest eyes in her family.
- Ⓒ Emma can eat a lot of food.

② I "put my foot in my mouth" when I said that I thought bologna sandwiches were disgusting. The boy next to me was eating one. What did I mean?

- Ⓕ I felt bad about what I said.
- Ⓖ I was so hungry, I could eat my foot.
- Ⓗ Bologna actually is my favorite.

③ Peyton and Noelle were laughing while working on the computer. Mr. Kane told them to "can it." What did he want them to do?

- Ⓐ Turn off the computer.
- Ⓑ Stop laughing.
- Ⓒ Go get their lunches.

④ Mrs. Daniels said I was "on the right track" to figuring out the math problem. What did she mean?

- Ⓕ I was only using my right hand to work on the problem.
- Ⓖ I was making too much noise while working.
- Ⓗ I was doing the problem correctly so far.

119

Read the e-mail below. Then answer the questions on the next page. You may look back at this page as you answer the questions.

Fiona Barnett

From: Fiona Barnett [fbarnett@home.com]
Sent: Wednesday, January 21, 2004 11:07 AM
To: jhathaway@orb.com

Hi Jenna,

My parents bought four tickets to the ice-skating show on Saturday. They told me I could invite a friend. If you're not busy, would you like to go? Ask your parents and then let me know! It should be a lot of fun. There will be amateur and professional skaters. My parents said we could eat dinner there too! Hope you can go. Talk to you soon!

Fiona

Name _____

1 **Who is the person receiving this e-mail?**

Ⓐ Fiona

Ⓑ Jenna

Ⓒ Jenna's parents

Ⓓ Fiona's parents

2 **When was this e-mail sent?**

Ⓕ Wednesday

Ⓖ Thursday

Ⓗ Friday

Ⓙ Saturday

3 **What is the purpose of this e-mail?**

Ⓐ to ask Jenna to go ice-skating on Saturday

Ⓑ to ask Jenna's parents to dinner

Ⓒ to ask Jenna to go to an ice-skating show

4 **What is jhathaway@orb.com?**

Ⓕ a street address

Ⓖ a post office box number

Ⓗ an e-mail address

Ⓙ a website

121

Name _____

Read the two sentences. Fill in the bubble next to the word that will make sense in *both* sentences.

1 Alyssa _____ a promise.
Yuan fell and _____ his arm.

Ⓐ made
Ⓑ hurt
Ⓒ broke

3 She wears a ring on her _____ hand.
Yesterday, Father _____ on a trip.

Ⓐ right
Ⓑ went
Ⓒ left

2 Mr. Johnson was a _____ man.
What _____ of pie do you want?

Ⓕ nice
Ⓖ kind
Ⓗ slice

4 I have my own _____ to sleep in.
Do you have _____ for this blanket?

Ⓕ bed
Ⓖ room
Ⓗ book

Name _____

 Last night the thief escaped from the dungeon. The dungeon was underneath the stairway.

How can these sentences be combined without changing the meaning?

Ⓐ Last night the thief escaped from the dungeon and went underneath the stairway.

Ⓑ Last night the thief escaped from the dungeon that was underneath the stairway.

Ⓒ The dungeon underneath the stairway is where the thief escaped to.

 The gorillas chased one another. They were running through the rain forest.

How can these sentences be combined without changing the meaning?

Ⓕ The gorillas chased one another while running through the rain forest.

Ⓖ The gorillas chased one another, but didn't run through the rain forest.

Ⓗ Through the rain forest gorillas chased.

123

Name _____

Look carefully at each group of words. Then choose the compound word (two words put together.)

1
- Ⓐ heavenly
- Ⓑ returning
- Ⓒ everything
- Ⓓ worked

2
- Ⓕ friendly
- Ⓖ thoughtful
- Ⓗ preflight
- Ⓙ nothing

3
- Ⓐ underground
- Ⓑ slowly
- Ⓒ darkness
- Ⓓ wonderful

4
- Ⓕ longest
- Ⓖ depart
- Ⓗ valuable
- Ⓙ yourself

124

Name _____

Fill in the bubble under the _complete subject_ of each sentence.

1 Ten fourth grade boys   played baseball.
     Ⓐ   Ⓑ

2 Her voice   was   very loud.
     Ⓕ   Ⓖ   Ⓗ

3 Robert   wants   a new jacket.
     Ⓐ   Ⓑ   Ⓒ

4 The red rooster   crowed   this morning.
     Ⓕ   Ⓖ   Ⓗ

Fill in the bubble under the _simple subject_ of each sentence.

5 Ten fourth grade boys played baseball.
     Ⓐ   Ⓑ Ⓒ   Ⓓ

6 Her   voice   was   very loud.
     Ⓕ   Ⓖ   Ⓗ   Ⓙ

7 Robert   wants   a   new   jacket.
     Ⓐ   Ⓑ   Ⓒ   Ⓓ

8 The red   rooster   crowed   this morning.
     Ⓕ   Ⓖ   Ⓗ   Ⓙ

125

Name _____

Fill in the bubble next to the sentence that is capitalized correctly.

1

Ⓐ The gentleman asked, "Is your brother at home?"

Ⓑ The Gentleman asked, "Is your brother at home?"

Ⓒ The gentleman asked, "Is your Brother at home?"

2

Ⓕ Cary's father traveled to germany every year.

Ⓖ Cary's father traveled to Germany every year.

Ⓗ Cary's Father traveled to Germany every year.

3

Ⓐ Her favorite book was *Mrs. Monk's Miracle*.

Ⓑ Her favorite book was *Mrs. Monk's miracle*.

Ⓒ Her favorite book was *Mrs. monk's miracle*.

4

Ⓕ The doctor's office was on sycamore drive.

Ⓖ The doctor's office was on Sycamore drive.

Ⓗ The doctor's office was on Sycamore Drive.

126

Name _____

1 Mark the word that has the same sound as <u>oy</u> in b<u>oy</u>.

Ⓐ maybe
Ⓑ foil
Ⓒ prey
Ⓓ grow

2 Mark the word that has the same sound as <u>wr</u> in <u>wr</u>ist.

Ⓕ why
Ⓖ wise
Ⓗ rise
Ⓙ wall

3 Mark the word that has the same sound as <u>kn</u> in <u>kn</u>ow.

Ⓐ nothing
Ⓑ kill
Ⓒ key
Ⓓ Kate

4 Mark the word that has the same sound as <u>a</u> in l<u>a</u>te.

Ⓕ market
Ⓖ key
Ⓗ at
Ⓙ rain

Name _____

We sat quietly in the library and read our books.

Which word from the sentence above is an adverb?

Ⓐ library

Ⓑ sat

Ⓒ quietly

Ⓓ read

Troy walks across the bridge to get to school.

Which word from the sentence above is a preposition?

Ⓕ walks

Ⓖ across

Ⓗ the

Ⓙ get

Name _____

Fill in the bubble next to the sentence that is punctuated correctly.

 1

Ⓐ The sixth-graders at our school have D.A.R.E. (Drug Abuse Resistance Education) every Monday afternoon.

Ⓑ The sixth-graders at our school have D.A.R.E. "Drug Abuse Resistance Education" every Monday afternoon.

Ⓒ The sixth-graders at our school have D.A.R.E. <u>Drug Abuse Resistance Education</u> every Monday afternoon.

Ⓓ The sixth-graders at our school have D.A.R.E. "<u>Drug Abuse Resistance Education</u>" every Monday afternoon.

 2

Ⓕ Don't throw that away, said Joey. "I want to keep it for my collection."

Ⓖ "Don't throw that away," said Joey. "I want to keep it for my collection.

Ⓗ "Don't throw that away, said Joey. I want to keep it for my collection."

Ⓙ "Don't throw that away," said Joey. "I want to keep it for my collection."

Read the passage below. Then answer the questions on the next page. You may look back at this page as you answer the questions.

Sandals are shoes that leave the tops of your feet open to the air. Do you wear sandals in the <u>summertime</u>? Perhaps your sandals are made of rubber or plastic with a strap between the toes. You may call them "thongs" or "flip-flops." Or maybe you wear leather sandals. Did you think sandals are the latest style? Well, if so, you are mistaken.

Sandals made of leather or plant fibers were worn in Egypt 4000 years ago and also by the ancient Romans and Greeks. They needed the sole to protect their feet when they walked on dirt paths or rocky roads. In some Asian countries people wore sandals with wooden soles, and many still do.

Name _____

1 **This passage *mainly* tells that —**

   Ⓐ everybody wears sandals.

   Ⓑ sandals are wooden shoes.

   Ⓒ sandals are not new.

2 **Sandals are always —**

   Ⓕ made of plastic.

   Ⓖ made of leather.

   Ⓗ open to the air.

3 **Choose the two words that make the word <u>summertime</u>.**

   Ⓐ summer + time

   Ⓑ sum + mertime

   Ⓒ some + time

4 **In each blank, write T if the statement is true. Write F if the statement is false.**

   ___ All shoes are sandals.

   ___ All people wear sandals.

   ___ All sandals have soles.

131

Name _____

Read each sentence and look at the <u>underlined words</u>. There may be a mistake in them. Select the best answer to correct the mistake. If there is no mistake, select *correct as is*.

1 Today <u>was more sunnier than</u> yesterday.

Ⓐ was sunnier than
Ⓑ was sunner than
Ⓒ was sunniest than
Ⓓ correct as is

2 Lupe <u>wrote and thank-you note</u> for the gift.

Ⓕ wrote a thank-you note
Ⓖ wrote an thank-you note
Ⓗ wrote any thank-you note
Ⓙ correct as is

3 Ellen <u>fell down and hurting</u> her knee.

Ⓐ fell down and hurted
Ⓑ fell down and hurts
Ⓒ fell down and hurt
Ⓓ correct as is

4 You had better study <u>that words</u> again!

Ⓕ them words
Ⓖ those words
Ⓗ this words
Ⓙ correct as is

Name _____

Fill in the bubble next to the word (homophone) that correctly completes each sentence.

1 Did you _____ the bell ring?

    Ⓐ here

    Ⓑ hear

2 I ate _____ much.

    Ⓕ two

    Ⓖ too

    Ⓗ to

3 How many _____ are in a day?

    Ⓐ hours

    Ⓑ ours

4 Jorge will _____ a letter to his uncle.

    Ⓕ right

    Ⓖ write

    Ⓗ rite

5 These shoes are _____.

    Ⓐ new

    Ⓑ knew

6 She _____ the bed with clean sheets.

    Ⓕ made

    Ⓖ maid

133

Name _____

In each group, fill in the bubble in front of the words that make a *complete sentence*.

1
- Ⓐ a ball of yarn
- Ⓑ the dog barked
- Ⓒ far, far away
- Ⓓ in the dark woods

2
- Ⓕ Grandpa built my tree house
- Ⓖ the cup of cocoa
- Ⓗ around the corner
- Ⓙ because he wants

3
- Ⓐ a long time ago
- Ⓑ one of the boys
- Ⓒ he said to me
- Ⓓ Chloe likes apple pie

4
- Ⓕ after the noon recess
- Ⓖ every once in a while
- Ⓗ Mark found the lost puppy
- Ⓙ He and I

Name _____

For each item below, look at the <u>underlined word</u>. Use the prefix or suffix to determine the meaning of the entire word.

❶ The word <u>reshow</u> means —

Ⓐ shown.

Ⓑ show again.

Ⓒ showing now.

Ⓓ show.

❷ The word <u>beautiful</u> means —

Ⓕ good looking.

Ⓖ ugly.

Ⓗ full of beauty.

Ⓙ beauty.

❸ The word <u>careless</u> means —

Ⓐ cared.

Ⓑ full of care.

Ⓒ without care.

Ⓓ caring.

❹ The word <u>displeased</u> means —

Ⓕ not pleased.

Ⓖ happy.

Ⓗ very pleased.

Ⓙ not wishing.

135

Name _____

Mark the bubble next to the sentence that goes *best* on the blank line in each paragraph.

❶ _____ **His neck was cut from being in a fight. He wouldn't eat and his bark sounded different. She was worried about him.**

Ⓐ Caroline's dog needed a bath.

Ⓑ Caroline's dog needed to go to the vet.

Ⓒ Caroline needed to feed her dog.

❷ **To do a book report on the computer, you must first read the book and think about it.** _____ **Then start your word processing program. Now you are ready to write. When you are satisfied with the report, print it out.**

Ⓕ Type in your report.

Ⓖ Next, turn the computer on.

Ⓗ Print out your report.

Name _____

Read the paragraph. Fill in the bubble by your answer. Then follow the written instruction below.

Fared's mother told him there were other ways to handle bullies without fighting. Fared wanted to fight, but he put up with Mario for months and months. One day Fared's mother watched as Mario teased and teased, poking and prodding, and never stopping. Finally,...

❶ What do you think happened next?

Ⓐ Mario went home.

Ⓑ Fared still wouldn't fight.

Ⓒ Fared poked and prodded back.

❷ On the lines below, write a few words telling why you chose your answer above.

_____

_____

_____

BELLWORK Reading/Language Arts • Level 4

Read the passage below. Then answer the following questions.

My dog, Lucy, is still just a little puppy. She gets excited over the smallest things. When we come home, she jumps around and almost does somersaults. When we give her a new toy or treat, she jumps on our laps and licks our ears. Last night, when we got out her food to feed her, she got so excited that she flipped over, ran into her water bowl and dumped the whole thing on herself. I nearly died laughing. She was soaked, but still just as excited about dinner even though she was wet from head to toe.

❶ Which words in this passage form a hyperbole or an exaggeration of a statement?

Ⓐ licks our ears
Ⓑ flipped over
Ⓒ ran into her water bowl
Ⓓ died laughing

❷ Which of the following is an effect of Lucy getting so excited?

Ⓕ She gets dinner.
Ⓖ She dumps water on herself.
Ⓗ She gets a new toy.
Ⓙ She gets a treat.

Name _____

Read the passage below. Then answer the following questions.

A family <u>of</u> deer was walking <u>through</u> the forest <u>along</u> a stream.

$\quad\quad\;\;$1$\quad\quad\quad\quad\quad\quad\quad$2$\quad\quad\quad\quad\quad$3

They stopped to get a drink, <u>but</u> soon they heard some rustling in

$\quad\quad\quad\quad\quad\quad\quad\quad\quad\quad\;$4

the <u>nearby</u> bushes. Their ears perked up to catch any <u>sounds</u> of

$\quad\quad\;$5$\quad\quad\quad\quad\quad\quad\quad\quad\quad\quad\quad\quad\quad\quad\quad$6

danger. Quickly, the family <u>ran</u> away to <u>safety</u>.

$\quad\quad\quad\quad\quad\quad\quad\quad\quad\quad$7$\quad\quad\quad\quad$8

---

❶ Which numbered word above is a conjunction?

Ⓐ 1   Ⓒ 3

Ⓑ 2   Ⓓ 4

❷ Which numbered word above is a verb?

Ⓕ 5   Ⓗ 7

Ⓖ 6   Ⓙ 8

139

Name _____

For each item below, choose the word that *means the same or almost the same* (synonym) as the <u>underlined word</u>.

❶ a <u>make-believe</u> story

Ⓐ real
Ⓑ truth
Ⓒ imaginary
Ⓓ journal

❸ an <u>amazing</u> play

Ⓐ same
Ⓑ usual
Ⓒ ordinary
Ⓓ unusual

❷ a <u>gigantic</u> stadium

Ⓕ little
Ⓖ huge
Ⓗ small
Ⓙ laughing

❹ a <u>swift</u> current

Ⓕ fast
Ⓖ slow
Ⓗ sweet
Ⓙ swinging

140

Name _____

Read each sentence and look at the <u>underlined words</u>. There may be a mistake in them. Select the best answer to correct the mistake. If there is no mistake, select *correct as is*.

❶ All the toy <u>soldiers fell over</u>.

  Ⓐ soldiers fallen over

  Ⓑ soldiers have fell over

  Ⓒ soldiers falling over

  Ⓓ correct as is

❷ My brother <u>is leave home</u>.

  Ⓕ is left home

  Ⓖ is has left home

  Ⓗ is leaving home

  Ⓙ correct as is

❸ <u>She tooks</u> my lunch money!

  Ⓐ She taken

  Ⓑ She has took

  Ⓒ She took

  Ⓓ correct as is

❹ He talked so softly, I <u>couldn't have hear him</u>.

  Ⓕ couldn't heard him

  Ⓖ couldn't hearing him

  Ⓗ couldn't hear him

  Ⓙ correct as is

141

Read the passage below. Then answer the questions on the next page. You may look back at this page as you answer the questions.

Ken's Aunt Kay told him that when <u>she</u> was two, she got chocolate icing from her birthday cake all over her face and her new baby doll.

On her fifth birthday, her mother had a party for her and her friends at a park. She loved the new watercolor set her aunt gave her.

When she was eight years old, her birthday present was a kitten. However, it jumped out of the car and ran away before Kay ever saw it!

Kay and her friends went to an entertainment center on her tenth birthday. First, they rented skates and went round and round the outdoor rink. When they got tired, they rode the bumper boats. Then she opened her presents, and they all had hamburgers, cake, and ice cream.

On her eighteenth birthday, after being very sick, she came home from the hospital. That was the best present she had ever received.

Name _____

Fill in the bubble next to the *best* answer for each question.

1 **This passage is *mostly* about —**

Ⓐ Ken's birthdays.

Ⓑ birthday cake.

Ⓒ Kay's birthdays.

2 **Kay was unhappy on her eighth birthday because —**

Ⓕ she didn't have a party.

Ⓖ nobody came to the party.

Ⓗ she didn't get the kitten she wanted.

3 **Choose the last activity at the tenth birthday party.**

Ⓐ renting skates

Ⓑ eating cake and ice cream

Ⓒ riding the bumper boats

4 **In the first sentence, the word <u>she</u> refers to —**

Ⓕ Aunt Kay.

Ⓖ her mother.

Ⓗ the baby doll.

143

Name _____

1 The guide words from a dictionary page are:

ion — ivy

Which word below would be found on this page?

Ⓐ ibex   Ⓒ item

Ⓑ invite   Ⓓ icon

2 The guide words from a dictionary page are:

radio — ram

Which word below would be found on this page?

Ⓕ rabbit   Ⓗ race

Ⓖ rake   Ⓙ ramble

3 The guide words from a dictionary page are:

golf — grand

Which word below would be found on this page?

Ⓐ general   Ⓒ goose

Ⓑ glow   Ⓓ great

4 The guide words from a dictionary page are:

devote — dial

Which word below would be found on this page?

Ⓕ date   Ⓗ dime

Ⓖ deal   Ⓙ dew

144

Name _____

Fill in the bubble next to the correctly spelled word that fits the <u>underlined definition</u>.

1 <u>a day of the week</u>

Ⓐ Tewsday
Ⓑ Teusday
Ⓒ Tuesday

3 <u>another day of the week</u>

Ⓐ Wensday
Ⓑ Wednesday
Ⓒ Wenesday

2 <u>a month of the year</u>

Ⓕ January
Ⓖ Januwary
Ⓗ Janeuary

4 <u>another month of the year</u>

Ⓕ Febuary
Ⓖ February
Ⓗ Febuwary

Name _____

Use this index to choose the *best* answer to each question.

Cats
> body, 104
> breeds, 106
> care, 107
> wild, 109

1 On what page would you find out whether or not to give your cat a bath?

Ⓐ 104   Ⓒ 107
Ⓑ 106   Ⓓ 109

2 On what page would you read about cats that are not pets?

Ⓕ 104   Ⓗ 108
Ⓖ 106   Ⓙ 109

3 On what page would you find a picture of the bone structure of a cat?

Ⓐ 109   Ⓒ 104
Ⓑ 108   Ⓓ 106

4 On what page might you find a picture of a Siamese cat?

Ⓕ 104   Ⓗ 105
Ⓖ 106   Ⓙ 108

Name _____

Mark the bubble in front of the sentence that *best* combines the numbered sentences.

1 Hannah rode her bike. I rode my bike. We went to school.

Ⓐ Hannah and I rode our bikes to school.

Ⓑ Hannah rode her bike, and I rode my bike because we went to school.

Ⓒ Hannah rode her bike when I rode my bike, and we went to school.

---

2 The highway was new. There were no potholes. It was smooth.

Ⓕ The highway was new, and there were no potholes, and it was smooth.

Ⓖ The highway was new, or there were no potholes when it was smooth.

Ⓗ The new highway was smooth with no potholes.

Read both passages below. Then answer the questions on the next page. You may look back at this page as you answer the questions.

Sample A

Yosemite National Park

Yosemite National Park has a rich history of geology. Yosemite Valley is known for its landmark rock formations. Half Dome is perhaps the most recognized symbol of Yosemite. Some people even rock climb to the top. Yosemite National Park has massive and giant sequoia trees, and is also the home to a number of waterfalls. The wildlife and wildflowers are <u>plentiful</u>. Bears are hard to find though you might see them in forests and meadows. Deer and birds are most often seen. When wildflowers are blooming they are easy to find in the meadows. Although there are lakes and rivers, very few are easily accessible in the park. Yosemite National Park is a wonderful place to visit and explore.

Sample B

March 18, 2003

I had a wonderful experience at Yosemite National Park. I climbed to the top of one of the tallest waterfalls in the park which overlooked much of the park below. A guide took us to see Half Dome which is a giant rock formation within the park. There were many people who were climbing the rock, but I chose to look up at it instead. Then we walked down through the meadows and saw amazing wildflowers and some deer grazing along the side of a path. Our guide knew all about the different wildlife and shared everything she knew with us. We were told about the bears, but fortunately I never saw any! The park is an enormous place and there is so much to see. I had an amazing time that day!

148

Name _____

① Information from *both* samples tells that —

Ⓐ Half Dome is a rock formation in Yosemite National Park.

Ⓑ Yosemite National Park has giant sequoia trees.

Ⓒ guides can take you through the park.

---

② Which fact about Sample B lets you know that it is a journal entry and not a letter?

Ⓕ It doesn't have any pictures.

Ⓖ It looks hand-written.

Ⓗ It doesn't have a greeting or closing.

③ Sentence from Sample A

> The wildlife and wildflowers are <u>plentiful</u>.

The root word of <u>plentiful</u> means —

Ⓐ a small amount.

Ⓑ a large amount.

Ⓒ none at all.

---

④ You can tell from the title of Sample A that the author is going to —

Ⓕ describe a place.

Ⓖ teach you how to cook something.

Ⓗ persuade you to do something.

149

Name _____

1 Choose the word that tells *exactly how* the room *smelled*.

Ⓐ loud

Ⓑ busy

Ⓒ smoky

Ⓓ hard

2 Choose the word that tells *exactly how* the water *felt*.

Ⓕ warm

Ⓖ rainy

Ⓗ rusty

Ⓘ cloudy

3 Choose the words that tell *exactly what* Bob *heard*.

Ⓐ a bird

Ⓑ a distant sound

Ⓒ an owl hoot

Ⓓ an animal

4 Choose the words that tell *exactly what* Kimberly *saw*.

Ⓕ an animal

Ⓖ a shadow

Ⓗ a black cat

Ⓘ a myth

150

Name _____

Fill in the bubble in front of the answer that goes *best* in each sentence.

❶ I like science _____ than literature.

Ⓐ best
Ⓑ better
Ⓒ good
Ⓓ gooder

❷ James is the _____ runner in our class.

Ⓕ fast
Ⓖ fastest
Ⓗ faster
Ⓙ more fast

❸ My sister is _____ than I am.

Ⓐ the tallest
Ⓑ taller
Ⓒ more taller
Ⓓ tall

❹ Who do you think was the _____ President of all the Presidents?

Ⓕ great
Ⓖ greater
Ⓗ greatest
Ⓙ most greatest

151

Name _____

Use the dictionary entry and definitions to answer the questions below.

---

better (bet´ər) **1.** more valuable, excellent, or desirable than another. **2.** larger; greater. **3.** improved in health.

---

❶ **Which of the above meanings fits the sentence below?**

The sick puppy is <u>better</u> today.

Ⓐ Definition 1
Ⓑ Definition 2
Ⓒ Definition 3

❷ **Which of the above meanings fits the sentence below?**

She is a <u>better</u> swimmer than I am.

Ⓕ Definition 1
Ⓖ Definition 2
Ⓗ Definition 3

Name _____

Fill in the bubble in front of the answer that tells the *author's purpose*.

1 "A frog went courting, away did ride, huh-huh. A frog went courting, away did ride. Sword and pistol by his side, huh-huh."

Unknown

Ⓐ to report   Ⓒ to entertain

Ⓑ to teach   Ⓓ to persuade

2 You should go to see your doctor. You are not eating enough. You don't seem to have much pep and you don't sleep well. Your doctor may be able to help you feel better.

Ⓕ to inform   Ⓗ to persuade

Ⓖ to entertain   Ⓙ to teach

3 A legend is a story that has been handed down from the past and is supposed to be based on fact. One of the most famous legends is the story of the Trojan Horse.

Ⓐ to teach   Ⓒ to persuade

Ⓑ to entertain   Ⓓ to invite

4 Dear Lauren,
Please come to visit us next weekend. We will have all sorts of games and a big dinner. It will be fun.

Ⓕ to teach   Ⓗ to report

Ⓖ to entertain   Ⓙ to invite

153

Read the passage below. Then answer the questions on the next page. You may look back at this page as you answer the questions.

Do you have houseplants in your home? Many people enjoy the beauty of green plants growing inside.

Now scientists are saying that houseplants can <u>improve</u> the quality of the air we breathe in our homes. It has been known for some time that plants absorb carbon dioxide and give off oxygen. Some kinds of plants absorb <u>formaldehyde</u> and other dangerous gases found in paint, plastics, and modern building materials.

Most houseplants are easy to grow. They need plenty of light and water just as you do. An occasional feeding helps them to grow and stay healthy.

You can grow a beautiful houseplant from the cut top of a carrot or a pineapple. If you suspend a sweet potato in a glass of water by toothpicks, you will soon have a very long vine.

And maybe you'll breathe easier too.

Name _____

1 From this passage you can tell that houseplants —

Ⓐ can put more oxygen into the air.

Ⓑ absorb gasoline.

Ⓒ do not need much light.

3 To <u>improve</u> means —

Ⓐ to experiment.

Ⓑ to make better.

Ⓒ to show you are right.

2 From this passage you can tell that <u>formaldehyde</u> is —

Ⓕ paint.

Ⓖ a dangerous gas.

Ⓗ building material.

4 Houseplants need —

Ⓕ plastic.

Ⓖ toothpicks.

Ⓗ light and water.

Name _____

Fill in the bubble next to the answer that correctly completes each sentence.

1 **The robot raised _____ hand.**

Ⓐ it's

Ⓑ its'

Ⓒ it'

Ⓓ its

2 **Martin Luther King, Jr. was born on**
_____

Ⓕ January 15 1929.

Ⓖ January, 15 1929.

Ⓗ January 15, 1929.

Ⓙ January, 15, 1929.

3 **What is the name of the actor in that**
_____

Ⓐ movie.

Ⓑ movie

Ⓒ movie?

Ⓓ movie!

4 **Jonathon said, _____**

Ⓕ Get out of here.

Ⓖ Get out of here?

Ⓗ "Get out of here"

Ⓙ "Get out of here!"

Name _____

Read each paragraph. Then fill in the bubble next to the sentence that goes *best* in the paragraph.

---

1 **Although it is wintertime where we live, the stores are selling fresh strawberries from South America.**

_____

Ⓐ When it is winter here, it is summer in South America.

Ⓑ Strawberries cost too much.

Ⓒ When strawberries are ripe, we go out and pick them.

---

2 _____

The paramedics came and took her to the hospital. It took several weeks before she could walk without using crutches.

Ⓕ Elizabeth played in her playhouse.

Ⓖ Elizabeth fell and broke her leg.

Ⓗ Elizabeth liked to climb in trees.

BELLWORK Reading/Language Arts • Level 4

Name _____

Read each set of sentences and decide if one of the <u>underlined words</u> is spelled *incorrectly*, or if there is *no mistake*. Choose your answer and fill in the bubble.

 1

Ⓐ The <u>croud</u> yelled, "Hooray!"

Ⓑ How much <u>information</u> does he need from me?

Ⓒ We went to a wonderful <u>concert</u>.

Ⓓ no mistake

 2

Ⓕ The ducks were <u>waiding</u> in the pond.

Ⓖ Marianne's birthday is in <u>August</u>.

Ⓗ How many <u>tickets</u> do I need?

Ⓙ no mistake

 3

Ⓐ Kelly <u>received</u> an award today.

Ⓑ We need a new <u>mowse</u> for our computer.

Ⓒ <u>Autumn</u> is the season between summer and winter.

Ⓓ no mistake

 4

Ⓕ The bird costs <u>twise</u> as much as the fish.

Ⓖ My sister <u>hid</u> in a tree at the park.

Ⓗ A scout will be a <u>loyal</u> and true friend.

Ⓙ no mistake

158

Name _____

Read the numbered sentence and look at the <u>underlined word</u>. Then choose the other sentence in which the <u>underlined word</u> is used in the same way.

❶ She placed an <u>order</u> over the phone.

Ⓐ Please list in alphabetical <u>order</u>.
Ⓑ The candy machine was out of <u>order</u>.
Ⓒ Your <u>order</u> will be mailed by Tuesday.
Ⓓ She worked in <u>order</u> to pay for college.

❷ My mom is now <u>branch</u> manager at the bank.

Ⓕ The <u>branch</u> fell from the tree.
Ⓖ Turn left at the <u>branch</u> in the road.
Ⓗ He wants to <u>branch</u> out by opening another store.
Ⓙ Our library <u>branch</u> will be closed on the holiday.

❸ I like to <u>draw</u> animals.

Ⓐ The cowboy said, "<u>Draw</u>!"
Ⓑ My lawyer will <u>draw</u> up the contract.
Ⓒ Please <u>draw</u> a graph.
Ⓓ Let's <u>draw</u> straws to see who goes first.

❹ Our <u>coach</u> is Mr. Morgan.

Ⓕ The <u>coach</u> was pulled by two horses.
Ⓖ We will fly in <u>coach</u>, not first class.
Ⓗ I would like to <u>coach</u> a team someday.
Ⓙ The school hired a new <u>coach</u>.

159

Name _____

Fill in the bubble in front of the pronoun that refers to the <u>underlined word or words</u>.

1 <u>**Mr. Kim**</u> **read to us from _____ newspaper.**

- Ⓐ it
- Ⓑ his
- Ⓒ him
- Ⓓ her

2 **The <u>books</u> were lost so we looked for _____.**

- Ⓕ her
- Ⓖ it
- Ⓗ these
- Ⓙ them

3 <u>**Bob and John**</u> **brought _____ lunches.**

- Ⓐ his
- Ⓑ these
- Ⓒ those
- Ⓓ their

4 **Give me some <u>money</u>. I need _____.**

- Ⓕ me
- Ⓖ you
- Ⓗ it
- Ⓙ them

160

Name _____

Mark the mistakes in the following personal letter. Put ≡ under letters that should be capitals. Put ^ to show where punctuation marks have been omitted. Can you find twenty (20) mistakes?

135 east main street

florence south carolina 29504

July 1 2005

dear mama and daddy

   I am having a good time at camp yesterday we went swimming

today Im going to make a surprise for you i miss both of you.

      Love

      Courtney

Name _____

Fill in the bubble next to the word that correctly completes each sentence.

1 I don't want _____ trouble with you.

Ⓐ any
Ⓑ no
Ⓒ none

2 Julie doesn't have _____ time.

Ⓕ any
Ⓖ no
Ⓗ none

3 We don't have _____ extra desks.

Ⓐ any
Ⓑ none
Ⓒ no

4 Kate has _____ money to buy candy.

Ⓕ no
Ⓖ any
Ⓗ none

Name _____

For each item below, choose the word that *means the same or almost the same* (synonym) as the underlined word.

1 **regular** means —

ⓐ usual
ⓑ regret
ⓒ special
ⓓ since

2 **famous** means —

ⓕ known
ⓖ family
ⓗ fare
ⓙ film

3 **frozen** means —

ⓐ frame
ⓑ icy
ⓒ fright
ⓓ froth

4 **answered** means —

ⓕ angel
ⓖ replied
ⓗ report
ⓙ people

163

Name _____

Fill in the bubble next to the answer that *best* completes each sentence correctly.

❶ Mom won't let me eat popcorn _____.

Ⓐ with lots of butter

Ⓑ can't cook

Ⓒ good for me

Ⓓ the microwave

❷ Galene and I _____ to camp together last year.

Ⓕ come

Ⓖ has come

Ⓗ came

Ⓙ done came

❸ We _____ lunch at noon.

Ⓐ will have

Ⓑ had have

Ⓒ has had

Ⓓ having

❹ The flower blossoms _____ now.

Ⓕ not blooming

Ⓖ are beautiful

Ⓗ often

Ⓙ healthy

Name _____

Read each sentence and look at the underlined words. There may be a mistake in them.
Select the best answer to correct the mistake. If there is no mistake, select *correct as is*.

---

1 **The chorus sunged** three patriotic songs.

   Ⓐ The chorus sing

   Ⓑ The chorus singed

   Ⓒ The chorus sang

   Ⓓ correct as is

---

2 **The gull flown** gracefully over the ocean.

   Ⓕ The gull flew

   Ⓖ The gull flyed

   Ⓗ The gull flied

   Ⓙ correct as is

---

3 He **has already eaten** his dinner.

   Ⓐ has already ate

   Ⓑ has already eated

   Ⓒ has already eating

   Ⓓ correct as is

---

4 **She bringing** her bulldog for "show-and-tell."

   Ⓕ She bringed

   Ⓖ She brang

   Ⓗ She brought

   Ⓙ correct as is

165

Read the passage below. Then answer the questions on the next page. You may look back at this page as you answer the questions.

I try and try to <u>photograph</u>
a butterfly in spring.
I want to get a picture
of its outspread wing.

But every time the camera
is ready at my eye,
the lovely creature won't sit still;
I watch it "flutter by."

Name _____

① **The word <u>photograph</u> means to —**

Ⓐ make a chart.

Ⓑ take a picture.

Ⓒ talk on the phone.

③ **To watch it "flutter by" means —**

Ⓐ to see it sit still.

Ⓑ to see it fly away.

Ⓒ to see it spread its wings.

② **You can tell the author thinks —**

Ⓕ butterflies are beautiful.

Ⓖ butterflies sit still.

Ⓗ butterflies are easy to photograph.

④ **In each group, circle the words that rhyme.**

photograph	camera
spring	eye
picture	still
wing	by

167

Name _____

In each group, fill in the bubble in front of the word that does *not* belong.

❶
- Ⓐ before
- Ⓑ after
- Ⓒ during
- Ⓓ but

❷
- Ⓕ beautiful
- Ⓖ ugly
- Ⓗ public
- Ⓙ pretty

❸
- Ⓐ grassy
- Ⓑ lefty
- Ⓒ flowery
- Ⓓ leafy

❹
- Ⓕ enough
- Ⓖ hot
- Ⓗ cool
- Ⓙ icy

Name _____

Fill in the bubble under the **_complete_**
predicate of each sentence.

Fill in the bubble under the **_simple_**
predicate of each sentence.

1 The   whistle   blew loudly.
    Ⓐ   Ⓑ   Ⓒ

5 The   whistle   blew   loudly.
    Ⓐ   Ⓑ   Ⓒ   Ⓓ

2 Lindy and I   bought some new shoes.
      Ⓕ   Ⓖ

6 Lindy   and   I   bought   some new   shoes.
    Ⓕ   Ⓖ   Ⓗ   Ⓙ

3 The old   car   ran a red light.
    Ⓐ   Ⓑ   Ⓒ

7 The old car   ran   a   red light.
    Ⓐ   Ⓑ   Ⓒ

4 Jack-o'-lanterns   glow on Halloween.
      Ⓕ   Ⓖ

8 Jack-o'-lanterns   glow   on   Halloween.
    Ⓕ   Ⓖ   Ⓗ

169

Name _____

Read each sentence and look at the <u>underlined words</u>. There may be a mistake in them.
Select the best answer to correct the mistake. If there is no mistake, select *correct as is*.

❶ I <u>don't want a trouble</u> from you!

  Ⓐ don't want any trouble

  Ⓑ don't want no trouble

  Ⓒ don't want none trouble

  Ⓓ correct as is

❷ <u>Vacation has comed</u> at last.

  Ⓕ Vacation has came

  Ⓖ Vacation has come

  Ⓗ Vacation has coming

  Ⓙ correct as is

❸ <u>Mr. Lee made</u> three dozen cookies.

  Ⓐ Mr. Lee maked

  Ⓑ Mr. Lee making

  Ⓒ Mr. Lee maded

  Ⓓ correct as is

❹ <u>Grandma and Grandpa is</u> not at home.

  Ⓕ Grandma and Grandpa isn't

  Ⓖ Grandma and Grandpa was

  Ⓗ Grandma and Grandpa were

  Ⓙ correct as is

Name _____

Fill in the bubble next to the correct spelling of the word that fits the <u>underlined definition</u>.

❶ <u>to think</u>

Ⓐ beliefe
Ⓑ believe
Ⓒ beleive

❸ <u>perhaps</u>

Ⓐ maby
Ⓑ mabe
Ⓒ maybe

❷ <u>forever</u>

Ⓕ always
Ⓖ allways
Ⓗ alweighs

❹ <u>spoke</u>

Ⓕ sayed
Ⓖ sad
Ⓗ said

Name _____

Fill in the bubble in front of the answer that tells where *best* to find the information.

❶ To find today's weather forecast, look in —

Ⓐ a glossary.

Ⓑ a dictionary.

Ⓒ a newspaper.

Ⓓ an encyclopedia.

❷ To find material for a report about orangutans, look in —

Ⓕ an atlas.

Ⓖ a newspaper.

Ⓗ a glossary.

Ⓙ an encyclopedia.

❸ To find the title of a book by Mark Twain, look in —

Ⓐ an encyclopedia.

Ⓑ a dictionary.

Ⓒ a library's catalog.

Ⓓ a glossary.

❹ To find the meaning of the word <u>government</u> in your textbook, look in —

Ⓕ the table of contents.

Ⓖ the glossary.

Ⓗ the title page.

Ⓙ the index.

Name _____

Fill in the bubble next to the answer that correctly completes each sentence.

1 **The root (base) of the word figured is —**

Ⓐ ed.
Ⓑ fig.
Ⓒ figure.
Ⓓ figured.

2 **The root (base) of the word speedily is —**

Ⓕ speed.
Ⓖ ily.
Ⓗ speedil.
Ⓙ speedily.

3 **The root (base) of the word sheepish is —**

Ⓐ heep.
Ⓑ she.
Ⓒ ish.
Ⓓ sheep.

4 **The root (base) of the word readable is —**

Ⓕ red.
Ⓖ read.
Ⓗ dable.
Ⓙ able.

173

Name _____

Mark the bubble next to the sentence that goes *best* on the blank line in each paragraph.

❶ **A new club was being formed.** _____ **Then they elected a secretary. Finally, they chose a treasurer to handle the money they hoped to make.**

Ⓐ Their first project was a lemonade stand.

Ⓑ First, they elected a president and a vice president.

Ⓒ It was called the Lemonade Club.

---

❷ _____ **He had a bat and a ball, but he needed a new mitt. How could he get one? He'd have to make some money. Maybe he could get a newspaper route.**

Ⓕ Martin got a newspaper route.

Ⓖ Martin loved to play baseball.

Ⓗ Martin's dad was out of town.

Name _____

Fill in the bubble next to the answer that correctly completes each sentence.

1 **The word <u>footbridge</u> means —**

Ⓐ a railroad bridge.

Ⓑ a bridge to walk on.

Ⓒ a walk in the forest.

Ⓓ a game.

2 **The word <u>worldwide</u> means —**

Ⓕ throughout the world.

Ⓖ a fat world.

Ⓗ in the United States.

Ⓙ in outer space.

3 **The word <u>bathtub</u> means —**

Ⓐ a washing machine.

Ⓑ a place to bathe.

Ⓒ a swimming place.

Ⓓ a bubble bath.

4 **The word <u>classmate</u> means —**

Ⓕ someone with class.

Ⓖ a lunchtime friend.

Ⓗ English class.

Ⓙ someone in the same class.

175

Read the passage below. Then answer the questions on the next page. You may look back at this page as you answer the questions.

They put me into a metallic suit with a clear plastic helmet. They shot me out of the cannon, and I headed for Palomar's moon. It was a fast flight, and the closer I got the greener the moon looked!

I landed in a deep <u>crater</u>, but the stuff under my feet and on the sides of the hole was so soft, I could dig steps in it, so I climbed right out of there. I looked for some trees or grass, but there were none!

Suddenly I realized I was hungry. "What am I going to eat?" I said to myself. (There was nobody else around to talk to, not even the man in the moon.)

I walked over to the nearest hill and sat down in the shade. It was still pretty hot, so I took off my helmet and gloves. Then I smelled something that smelled like food. I reached over and dug out a finger full of the green stuff and put it in my mouth to taste. What a surprising thing I found out. That moon really was made of green cheese!

❶ This passage is a form of —

Ⓐ drama.

Ⓑ nonfiction.

Ⓒ fiction.

❸ He talked to himself because —

Ⓐ he liked the sound of his voice.

Ⓑ he smelled food.

Ⓒ no one else was there.

❷ The word <u>crater</u> means —

Ⓕ a hole in the ground.

Ⓖ a big box.

Ⓗ a maker of boxes.

❹ The color of the cheese made —

Ⓕ grass and trees grow.

Ⓖ the moon look green.

Ⓗ the food taste good.

Name _____

Below is a timeline of five missions founded in California. Look at the timeline, then answer the questions that follow.

Missions of California

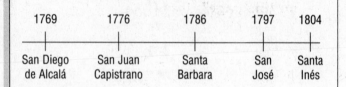

1769	1776	1786	1797	1804
San Diego de Alcalá	San Juan Capistrano	Santa Barbara	San José	Santa Inés

❶ In what year was the mission in San José founded?

Ⓐ 1769

Ⓑ 1786

Ⓒ 1797

Ⓓ 1804

❷ Which mission was founded before the mission in Santa Barbara?

Ⓕ San Diego de Alcalá

Ⓖ San José

Ⓗ Santa Inés

❸ This timeline shows a span of how many years?

Ⓐ 25

Ⓑ 35

Ⓒ 65

Ⓓ 73

Name _____

❶ The guide words from a dictionary page are:

admire — affable

Which word below would be found on this page?

Ⓐ action   Ⓒ afford

Ⓑ adverb   Ⓓ airplane

❷ The guide words from a dictionary page are:

recall — record

Which word below would be found on this page?

Ⓕ recede   Ⓗ recreate

Ⓖ reduce   Ⓙ red

❸ The guide words from a dictionary page are:

fester — figure

Which word below would be found on this page?

Ⓐ fee   Ⓒ face

Ⓑ file   Ⓓ fife

❹ The guide words from a dictionary page are:

teaspoon — tentacle

Which word below would be found on this page?

Ⓕ tone   Ⓗ tied

Ⓖ television   Ⓙ term

179

Read the recipe below. Then answer the questions on the next page. You may look back at this page as you answer the questions.

Recipe for:

Vanilla Sugar Cookies

Servings: About 3 dozen

Ingredients:

2½	cups of all-purpose flour
1	teaspoon of baking powder
½	teaspoon of salt
1	cup of granulated sugar
1	cup of butter
2	large egg yolks
1½	teaspoons of vanilla extract

What to do:

1. Preheat oven to 375 degrees.
2. In a large bowl, combine butter and sugar. Beat in the egg yolks. Beat in the vanilla extract.
3. In a separate bowl, combine all of the remaining dry ingredients. Gradually blend in the dry ingredients with the butter mixture. Cover and chill for one hour.
4. On a floured surface, roll out the dough. Using a cookie cutter, cut out cookies and place onto a greased cookie sheet.
5. Bake for 10-12 minutes, until golden. Transfer to wire racks to cool.

Name _____

1 This recipe tells how to make —

Ⓐ a main dish.

Ⓑ a vegetable.

Ⓒ a dessert.

Ⓓ an appetizer.

2 If you were to double this recipe, about how many cookies would you make?

Ⓕ 6 dozen

Ⓖ 5 dozen

Ⓗ 9 dozen

Ⓙ 2 dozen

3 What ingredients should you combine in a separate bowl?

Ⓐ butter, sugar, and flour

Ⓑ vanilla, egg yolks, and salt

Ⓒ flour, egg yolks, and vanilla

Ⓓ flour, baking powder, and salt

4 The recipe says to <u>preheat</u> the oven. What does preheat mean?

Ⓕ turn on the oven after you make the cookies

Ⓖ turn off the oven

Ⓗ turn on the oven before you make the cookies

181

Name _____

Mark the bubble in front of the sentence that *best* combines the numbered sentences.

❶ The radio was on. We were listening. It was rock and roll.

Ⓐ The radio was on, but we were listening to rock and roll.

Ⓑ We were listening to rock and roll on the radio.

Ⓒ The radio being on that we were listening, and it was rock and roll.

---

❷ I don't want to eat vegetables. I know I should eat vegetables. I don't like vegetables.

Ⓕ I don't want to eat, and I should eat, but I don't like vegetables.

Ⓖ I know I should eat vegetables even though I don't like them.

Ⓗ I don't want to eat, but I know I should, I should eat vegetables.

Name _____

Use the table of contents to choose the correct answer to each question.

TABLE OF CONTENTS

	Page
Clowns	3
The High-Wire Act	6
Elephant Parade.	10
The Lion Tamer.	12
Bareback Riding.	17

1 On what page would you find "The High-Wire Act"?

Ⓐ 6

Ⓑ 3

Ⓒ 10

2 A story that might tell about the training of wild cats begins on page —

Ⓕ 3.

Ⓖ 10.

Ⓗ 12.

3 Most of the stories in this book are probably about —

Ⓐ clowns.

Ⓑ animals.

Ⓒ the circus.

4 What would you probably be reading about on page 18?

Ⓕ lions

Ⓖ riding horses

Ⓗ parades

183

Name _____

Fill in the bubble next to the word that is *closest in meaning* to the <u>underlined word</u>.

❶ The word <u>went</u> is *closest in meaning* to —

Ⓐ stay.

Ⓑ go.

Ⓒ we.

Ⓓ arrive.

❷ The word <u>were</u> is *closest in meaning* to —

Ⓕ wear.

Ⓖ are.

Ⓗ we.

Ⓙ wire.

❸ The word <u>found</u> is *closest in meaning* to —

Ⓐ fine.

Ⓑ foot.

Ⓒ find.

Ⓓ fund.

❹ The word <u>took</u> is *closest in meaning* to —

Ⓕ leave.

Ⓖ too.

Ⓗ take.

Ⓙ talk.

184

Name _____

Use the dictionary entry and definitions to answer the questions below.

---

cream (krēm´) **1.** the thick, fatty part of milk. **2.** to make into a smooth mixture. **3.** a special mixture that is put on the skin. **4.** yellowish-white. **5.** the best part of anything.

---

1 Which of the above meanings fits the sentence below?

My mother painted the walls a <u>cream</u> color.

Ⓐ Definition **1**

Ⓑ Definition **2**

Ⓒ Definition **3**

Ⓓ Definition **4**

Ⓔ Definition **5**

2 Which of the above meanings fits the sentence below?

My father drinks coffee with <u>cream</u>.

Ⓕ Definition **1**

Ⓖ Definition **2**

Ⓗ Definition **3**

Ⓙ Definition **4**

Ⓚ Definition **5**

185

Read the passage below. Then answer the questions on the next page. You may look back at this page as you answer the questions.

In the early part of the twentieth century, most clothing was made of cotton, wool, or linen. Cottons and linens were washed with hot water and soap. After being hung on a line to dry, they were very wrinkled. The clothes were <u>sprinkled</u> with water and allowed to dampen evenly by rolling them in a towel. Then very heavy "flatirons" were heated on the top of a stove to iron out the wrinkles.

When electric irons with controlled heat settings came into use, it was much easier to avoid scorching the clothes and ironing was less tiresome. Electric irons were not so heavy.

Next came the steam and dry irons. By that time many combinations of textiles were in common use. Most of them required no ironing at all.

Now very light steamers can get rid of wrinkles without even using an ironing board, and many clothes need no ironing.

1 Flatirons could scorch clothes because —

Ⓐ they were not hot enough.

Ⓑ they had no heat controls.

Ⓒ they were too flat.

Ⓓ they had no steam.

2 In this passage, <u>sprinkled</u> means —

Ⓕ it rained lightly.

Ⓖ a fountain.

Ⓗ wet with a little water.

Ⓙ soaked.

3 The *best* title for this passage is —

Ⓐ "The Twentieth Century."

Ⓑ "The History of Irons."

Ⓒ "Cotton Clothing."

Ⓓ "Electric Irons."

4 Number the following inventions in the correct order.

_____ steam/dry irons

_____ electric irons

_____ flatirons

_____ steamers

187

Name _____

Fill in the bubble in front of the sentence that is correctly written.

 1

Ⓐ I like science gooder than literature.

Ⓑ I like science best than literature.

Ⓒ I like science better than literature.

 2

Ⓕ Today the paper is latest than yesterday.

Ⓖ Yesterday the sun set later than today.

Ⓗ James is a fast runner than Mark.

 3

Ⓐ My sister is more bigger than I am.

Ⓑ My sister is the tallest of the two of us.

Ⓒ My sister can do math better than I.

 4

Ⓕ The sum of 2 and 4 is greater than 5.

Ⓖ That was the great game we ever played.

Ⓗ Who do you think was the greater President of all the Presidents?

Name _____

Fill in the bubble next to the word that correctly completes each sentence.

1 I'm going over to _____ house.

Ⓐ Marita's
Ⓑ Maritas
Ⓒ Marita
Ⓓ Maritas'

2 I can wear my _____ clothes.

Ⓕ sister
Ⓖ sisters
Ⓗ sister,s
Ⓙ sister's

3 Jane has two _____.

Ⓐ brother's
Ⓑ brothers
Ⓒ brother
Ⓓ brothers'

4 The bus driver made four _____.

Ⓕ stops
Ⓖ stop
Ⓗ stop's
Ⓙ stops'

189

Name _____

Fill in the bubble next to the one that *means the same* as the <u>underlined word</u>.

1 After a month in the gold mine, they gave up the <u>hopeless</u> search.

Ⓐ still hoping
Ⓑ hopping
Ⓒ without hope
Ⓓ with hope

2 Mr. Pham is a very <u>careful</u> driver.

Ⓕ full of care
Ⓖ without care
Ⓗ in a car
Ⓙ a car full

Fill in the bubble next to the one that completes each sentence correctly.

3 She _____ home an hour ago.

Ⓐ has went
Ⓑ gone
Ⓒ went
Ⓓ going

4 We _____ out the trash on Thursday.

Ⓕ taken
Ⓖ have took
Ⓗ taking
Ⓙ took

Name _____

Fill in the bubble next to the sentence that goes *best* on the blank line in each paragraph.

❶ _____ **Dad likes to watch sports. My little brother likes cartoons. Mother won't let me watch wrestling, but she watches country dancing.**

Ⓐ Mother sings country songs.

Ⓑ Everybody in our house likes to watch TV.

Ⓒ Cartoons are not always funny.

❷ **Billy had to write a book report.** _____ **He asked the librarian for help. She showed him several books and told him something about their plots.**

Ⓕ Billy got an "A" on his report.

Ⓖ He went to the library.

Ⓗ He chose a science fiction book.

Name _____

Fill in the bubble in front of the meaning of the <u>underlined prefix or suffix</u>.

❶ work<u>er</u>

- Ⓐ work
- Ⓑ again
- Ⓒ one who
- Ⓓ pleasure

❷ <u>de</u>part

- Ⓕ from
- Ⓖ full of
- Ⓗ again
- Ⓙ stay

❸ <u>non</u>breakable

- Ⓐ one who
- Ⓑ full of
- Ⓒ not
- Ⓓ against

❹ soft<u>en</u>

- Ⓕ one who
- Ⓖ to make
- Ⓗ hard
- Ⓙ soft

Name _____

Fill in the bubble in front of the correct spelling for the word that fits the <u>underlined definition</u>.

1 <u>**a soldier in olden times**</u>

   Ⓐ night
   Ⓑ nite
   Ⓒ knight

2 <u>**a state in the United States**</u>

   Ⓕ Main
   Ⓖ Maine
   Ⓗ Mane

3 <u>**an idea**</u>

   Ⓐ thought
   Ⓑ thawed
   Ⓒ throught

4 <u>**to clean a person or animal**</u>

   Ⓕ bath
   Ⓖ baeth
   Ⓗ bathe

193

Name _____

Choose the word that *best* connects the thoughts in each of the following sentences. Then *write* each new sentence on the line and add punctuation where necessary.

1 She is a hero. She saved two people.

Ⓐ whether   Ⓑ or   Ⓒ because   Ⓓ but

_____

2 They could cook and eat at home. They could go out for dinner.

Ⓕ because   Ⓖ and   Ⓗ or   Ⓙ while

_____

3 Sam played baseball. Gavin played football.

Ⓐ because   Ⓑ but   Ⓒ for   Ⓓ or

_____

4 His dad liked fishing. Han did not.

Ⓕ although   Ⓖ or   Ⓗ because   Ⓙ nor

_____

Name _____

Fill in the bubble under the *simple subject* of each sentence.

1 The house is white.
  Ⓐ   Ⓑ   Ⓒ   Ⓓ

2 Jane went on vacation.
  Ⓕ   Ⓖ   Ⓗ   Ⓙ

3 Our pencils are sharp.
  Ⓐ   Ⓑ   Ⓒ   Ⓓ

4 Their dresses look pretty.
  Ⓕ   Ⓖ   Ⓗ   Ⓙ

Fill in the bubble under the *simple predicate* of each sentence.

5 The house is white.
  Ⓐ   Ⓑ   Ⓒ   Ⓓ

6 Jane went on vacation.
  Ⓕ   Ⓖ   Ⓗ   Ⓙ

7 Our pencils are sharp.
  Ⓐ   Ⓑ   Ⓒ   Ⓓ

8 Their dresses look pretty.
  Ⓕ   Ⓖ   Ⓗ   Ⓙ

195

Read the passage below. Then answer the questions on the next page. You may look back at this page as you answer the questions.

Bessie was a Jersey cow, although she didn't look like one. In fact, she was purple! Mr. Mason bought her in spite of her color because she was the least expensive Jersey cow he could find. He believed the papers that said she was a Jersey and should produce lots of rich milk like all other Jerseys.

At his farm he gave her lots of good food, plenty of water, and a clean warm place to sleep. Bessie proved true to her papers. She gave lots of milk for the farmer and his family. In fact, they had extra milk, cream, and butter to sell to people who lived in town.

Mr. Mason knew she was a good cow, but he didn't know she could talk. However, when she heard the neighbors laughing at her because she was purple, they were amazed to hear her say, "After all, it's what's on the inside that counts!"

196

❶ Mr. Mason bought Bessie because —

Ⓐ she was purple.

Ⓑ she was a Jersey cow.

Ⓒ she could talk.

❸ Bessie's papers said she should —

Ⓐ be purple.

Ⓑ be able to talk.

Ⓒ give lots of milk.

❷ This passage is —

Ⓕ nonfiction.

Ⓖ a fable.

Ⓗ a poem.

❹ The *moral* of this passage is that —

Ⓕ all cows should be purple.

Ⓖ looks are most important.

Ⓗ what we do is more important than how we look.

197

Name _____

Number each group of words below in alphabetical order.

❶

___ camera
___ cinema
___ comical
___ cuteness

❸

___ shout
___ shall
___ shell
___ shine

❷

___ shall
___ still
___ scale
___ small

❹

___ rather
___ richer
___ rougher
___ rounder

Name _____

In each group, fill in the bubble in front of the word that does *not* belong.

❶

Ⓐ night
Ⓑ evening
Ⓒ noon
Ⓓ today

❷

Ⓕ later
Ⓖ between
Ⓗ beside
Ⓙ atop

❸

Ⓐ plate
Ⓑ diet
Ⓒ dish
Ⓓ bowl

❹

Ⓕ otter
Ⓖ fisherman
Ⓗ whale
Ⓙ octopus

Name _____

Fill in the bubble next to the sentence that is punctuated and capitalized correctly.

1

Ⓐ She said, "you may not go."

Ⓑ She said, "You may not go."

Ⓒ she said, "You may not go."

2

Ⓕ "Yes, I will," she replied.

Ⓖ "yes, I will," she replied.

Ⓗ Yes, I will," She replied.

3

Ⓐ "a rose by any other name would smell as sweet."

Ⓑ "A rose by any other name would smell as sweet.

Ⓒ "A rose by any other name would smell as sweet."

4

Ⓕ Tom laughed out loud, that was funny, he said.

Ⓖ Tom laughed out loud. That was funny," he said.

Ⓗ Tom laughed out loud. "That was funny," he said.

200

Name _____

Fill in the bubble in front of the answer that tells the *best* place to find the information described.

1 To find out how to pronounce a word in your textbook, look in —

Ⓐ the title page.

Ⓑ the index.

Ⓒ the table of contents.

Ⓓ the glossary.

2 To find material for a report about Peru, look in —

Ⓕ a dictionary.

Ⓖ a title page.

Ⓗ an encyclopedia.

Ⓘ a diary.

3 To find the name of the author of a book you are reading, look at —

Ⓐ the table of contents.

Ⓑ the index.

Ⓒ the title page.

Ⓓ the glossary.

4 In a book about Peru, to find pages with information about llamas, look in —

Ⓕ the pictures.

Ⓖ the glossary.

Ⓗ the title page.

Ⓘ the index.

201

Name _____

Use the dictionary entry and definitions to answer the questions below.

guest (gest´) **1.** a person who is received at another's house; visitor. **2.** a person who is staying at a hotel or motel. **3.** a person invited to appear at a television show, concert, or the like.

1 Which of the above meanings fits the sentence below?

The opera singer was a <u>guest</u> on the talk show.

Ⓐ Definition **1**
Ⓑ Definition **2**
Ⓒ Definition **3**

2 Which of the above meanings fits the sentence below?

Melissa was my <u>guest</u> overnight.

Ⓕ Definition **1**
Ⓖ Definition **2**
Ⓗ Definition **3**

Name _____

Fill in the bubble next to the word that is *closest in meaning* to the underlined word.

1 Jack <u>ate</u> corn on the cob.

    Ⓐ hungry

    Ⓑ eat

    Ⓒ are

    Ⓓ plate

3 Mother said I <u>could</u> spend the night.

    Ⓐ count

    Ⓑ can

    Ⓒ charge

    Ⓓ coast

2 Jasmine <u>felt</u> the sting of the wasp.

    Ⓕ feel

    Ⓖ fell

    Ⓗ field

    Ⓙ fellow

4 My uncle <u>bought</u> me a new bicycle.

    Ⓕ taught

    Ⓖ buy

    Ⓗ sold

    Ⓙ bring

203

Name _____

Read the poem. Fill in the bubble by your answer. Then follow the written instruction below.

"Red sky in the morning,
Sailors take warning.
Red sky at night,
Sailor's delight."

❶ **If the writer sees a red sunrise, what does he think the weather will be like that day?**

Ⓐ sunny   Ⓑ calm   Ⓒ stormy

❷ **Write a few words on the lines below to tell what *you* think the weather will be like if you see a red sky at sunset.**

_____

_____

Page _____

A

1. Ⓐ Ⓑ Ⓒ Ⓓ Ⓔ
2. Ⓕ Ⓖ Ⓗ Ⓙ Ⓚ
3. Ⓐ Ⓑ Ⓒ Ⓓ Ⓔ
4. Ⓕ Ⓖ Ⓗ Ⓙ Ⓚ

Page _____

B

1. Ⓐ Ⓑ Ⓒ Ⓓ Ⓔ
2. Ⓕ Ⓖ Ⓗ Ⓙ Ⓚ
3. Ⓐ Ⓑ Ⓒ Ⓓ Ⓔ
4. Ⓕ Ⓖ Ⓗ Ⓙ Ⓚ

Page _____

C

1. Ⓐ Ⓑ Ⓒ Ⓓ Ⓔ
2. Ⓕ Ⓖ Ⓗ Ⓙ Ⓚ
3. Ⓐ Ⓑ Ⓒ Ⓓ Ⓔ
4. Ⓕ Ⓖ Ⓗ Ⓙ Ⓚ

Page _____

D

1. Ⓐ Ⓑ Ⓒ Ⓓ Ⓔ
2. Ⓕ Ⓖ Ⓗ Ⓙ Ⓚ
3. Ⓐ Ⓑ Ⓒ Ⓓ Ⓔ
4. Ⓕ Ⓖ Ⓗ Ⓙ Ⓚ

Page _____

E

1. Ⓐ Ⓑ Ⓒ Ⓓ Ⓔ
2. Ⓕ Ⓖ Ⓗ Ⓙ Ⓚ
3. Ⓐ Ⓑ Ⓒ Ⓓ Ⓔ
4. Ⓕ Ⓖ Ⓗ Ⓙ Ⓚ

Page _____

F

1. Ⓐ Ⓑ Ⓒ Ⓓ Ⓔ
2. Ⓕ Ⓖ Ⓗ Ⓙ Ⓚ
3. Ⓐ Ⓑ Ⓒ Ⓓ Ⓔ
4. Ⓕ Ⓖ Ⓗ Ⓙ Ⓚ

Page _____

G

1. Ⓐ Ⓑ Ⓒ Ⓓ Ⓔ
2. Ⓕ Ⓖ Ⓗ Ⓙ Ⓚ
3. Ⓐ Ⓑ Ⓒ Ⓓ Ⓔ
4. Ⓕ Ⓖ Ⓗ Ⓙ Ⓚ

Page _____

H

1. Ⓐ Ⓑ Ⓒ Ⓓ Ⓔ
2. Ⓕ Ⓖ Ⓗ Ⓙ Ⓚ
3. Ⓐ Ⓑ Ⓒ Ⓓ Ⓔ
4. Ⓕ Ⓖ Ⓗ Ⓙ Ⓚ

Page _____

I

1. Ⓐ Ⓑ Ⓒ Ⓓ Ⓔ
2. Ⓕ Ⓖ Ⓗ Ⓙ Ⓚ
3. Ⓐ Ⓑ Ⓒ Ⓓ Ⓔ
4. Ⓕ Ⓖ Ⓗ Ⓙ Ⓚ

Page _____

J

1. Ⓐ Ⓑ Ⓒ Ⓓ Ⓔ
2. Ⓕ Ⓖ Ⓗ Ⓙ Ⓚ
3. Ⓐ Ⓑ Ⓒ Ⓓ Ⓔ
4. Ⓕ Ⓖ Ⓗ Ⓙ Ⓚ

Page _____

K

1. Ⓐ Ⓑ Ⓒ Ⓓ Ⓔ
2. Ⓕ Ⓖ Ⓗ Ⓙ Ⓚ
3. Ⓐ Ⓑ Ⓒ Ⓓ Ⓔ
4. Ⓕ Ⓖ Ⓗ Ⓙ Ⓚ

Page _____

L

1. Ⓐ Ⓑ Ⓒ Ⓓ Ⓔ
2. Ⓕ Ⓖ Ⓗ Ⓙ Ⓚ
3. Ⓐ Ⓑ Ⓒ Ⓓ Ⓔ
4. Ⓕ Ⓖ Ⓗ Ⓙ Ⓚ

Page _____

A

1. Ⓐ Ⓑ Ⓒ Ⓓ Ⓔ
2. Ⓕ Ⓖ Ⓗ Ⓙ Ⓚ
3. Ⓐ Ⓑ Ⓒ Ⓓ Ⓔ
4. Ⓕ Ⓖ Ⓗ Ⓙ Ⓚ

Page _____

B

1. Ⓐ Ⓑ Ⓒ Ⓓ Ⓔ
2. Ⓕ Ⓖ Ⓗ Ⓙ Ⓚ
3. Ⓐ Ⓑ Ⓒ Ⓓ Ⓔ
4. Ⓕ Ⓖ Ⓗ Ⓙ Ⓚ

Page _____

C

1. Ⓐ Ⓑ Ⓒ Ⓓ Ⓔ
2. Ⓕ Ⓖ Ⓗ Ⓙ Ⓚ
3. Ⓐ Ⓑ Ⓒ Ⓓ Ⓔ
4. Ⓕ Ⓖ Ⓗ Ⓙ Ⓚ

Page _____

D

1. Ⓐ Ⓑ Ⓒ Ⓓ Ⓔ
2. Ⓕ Ⓖ Ⓗ Ⓙ Ⓚ
3. Ⓐ Ⓑ Ⓒ Ⓓ Ⓔ
4. Ⓕ Ⓖ Ⓗ Ⓙ Ⓚ

Page _____

E

1. Ⓐ Ⓑ Ⓒ Ⓓ Ⓔ
2. Ⓕ Ⓖ Ⓗ Ⓙ Ⓚ
3. Ⓐ Ⓑ Ⓒ Ⓓ Ⓔ
4. Ⓕ Ⓖ Ⓗ Ⓙ Ⓚ

Page _____

F

1. Ⓐ Ⓑ Ⓒ Ⓓ Ⓔ
2. Ⓕ Ⓖ Ⓗ Ⓙ Ⓚ
3. Ⓐ Ⓑ Ⓒ Ⓓ Ⓔ
4. Ⓕ Ⓖ Ⓗ Ⓙ Ⓚ

Page _____

G

1. Ⓐ Ⓑ Ⓒ Ⓓ Ⓔ
2. Ⓕ Ⓖ Ⓗ Ⓙ Ⓚ
3. Ⓐ Ⓑ Ⓒ Ⓓ Ⓔ
4. Ⓕ Ⓖ Ⓗ Ⓙ Ⓚ

Page _____

H

1. Ⓐ Ⓑ Ⓒ Ⓓ Ⓔ
2. Ⓕ Ⓖ Ⓗ Ⓙ Ⓚ
3. Ⓐ Ⓑ Ⓒ Ⓓ Ⓔ
4. Ⓕ Ⓖ Ⓗ Ⓙ Ⓚ

Page _____

I

1. Ⓐ Ⓑ Ⓒ Ⓓ Ⓔ
2. Ⓕ Ⓖ Ⓗ Ⓙ Ⓚ
3. Ⓐ Ⓑ Ⓒ Ⓓ Ⓔ
4. Ⓕ Ⓖ Ⓗ Ⓙ Ⓚ

Page _____

J

1. Ⓐ Ⓑ Ⓒ Ⓓ Ⓔ
2. Ⓕ Ⓖ Ⓗ Ⓙ Ⓚ
3. Ⓐ Ⓑ Ⓒ Ⓓ Ⓔ
4. Ⓕ Ⓖ Ⓗ Ⓙ Ⓚ

Page _____

K

1. Ⓐ Ⓑ Ⓒ Ⓓ Ⓔ
2. Ⓕ Ⓖ Ⓗ Ⓙ Ⓚ
3. Ⓐ Ⓑ Ⓒ Ⓓ Ⓔ
4. Ⓕ Ⓖ Ⓗ Ⓙ Ⓚ

Page _____

L

1. Ⓐ Ⓑ Ⓒ Ⓓ Ⓔ
2. Ⓕ Ⓖ Ⓗ Ⓙ Ⓚ
3. Ⓐ Ⓑ Ⓒ Ⓓ Ⓔ
4. Ⓕ Ⓖ Ⓗ Ⓙ Ⓚ